Little Passenger®

Activity Books, Activity Maps & More!

These games and puzzles are designed to make time fly while traveling!

Kid's
UNITED STATES
Atlas

Table Of Contents

Alabama	3	New Hampshire	31
Alaska	4	New Jersey	34
Arizona	5	New Mexico	35
Arkansas	6	New York	36
California	7	North Carolina	37
Colorado	8	North Dakota	38
Connecticut	9	Ohio	39
Delaware	10	Oklahoma	40
Florida	11	Oregon	41
Georgia	12	Pennsylvania	42
Hawaii	13	Rhode Island	43
Idaho	14	South Carolina	44
Illinois	15	South Dakota	45
Indiana	16	Tennessee	46
Iowa	17	Texas	47
Kansas	18	Utah	48
Kentucky	19	Vermont	49
Louisiana	20	Virginia	50
Maine	21	Washington	51
Maryland	22	West Virginia	52
Massachusetts	23	Wisconsin	53
Michigan	24	Wyoming	54
Minnesota	25	Canada	55
Mississippi	26	Mexico	56
Missouri	27	U.S.A. Map	32-33
Montana	28	Answer Pages	63-64
Nebraska	29	Index	57-62
Nevada	30		

Alabama
Heart Of Dixie, Camellia State

Crossword

Alabama's capital is Montgomery.
Use the grid coordinates and cities on
the map to complete the puzzle.

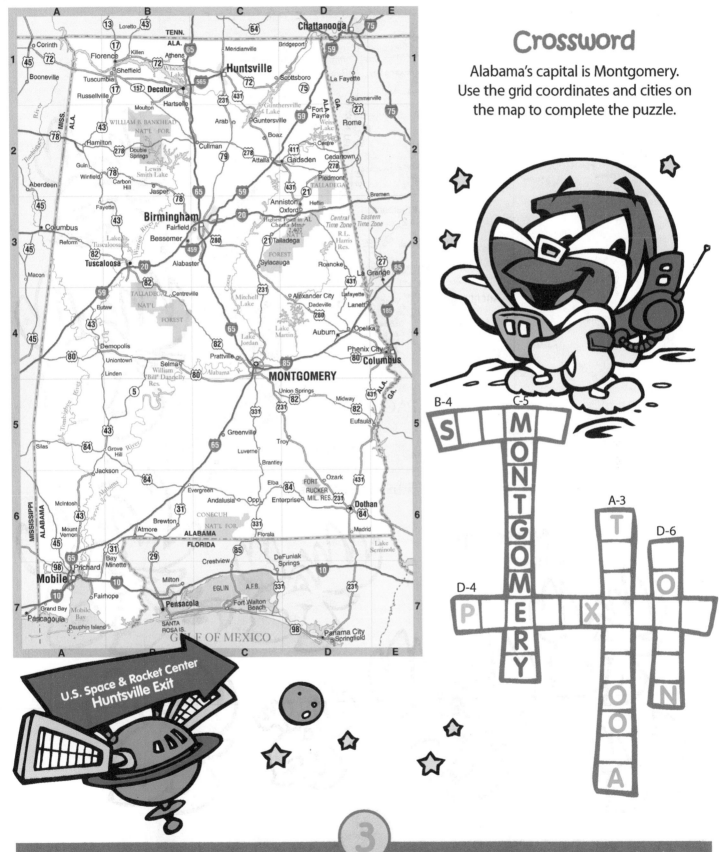

Capital City: Montgomery
State Bird: Yellowhammer
State Tree: Southern Pine
Statehood: 1819
State Flower: Camellia

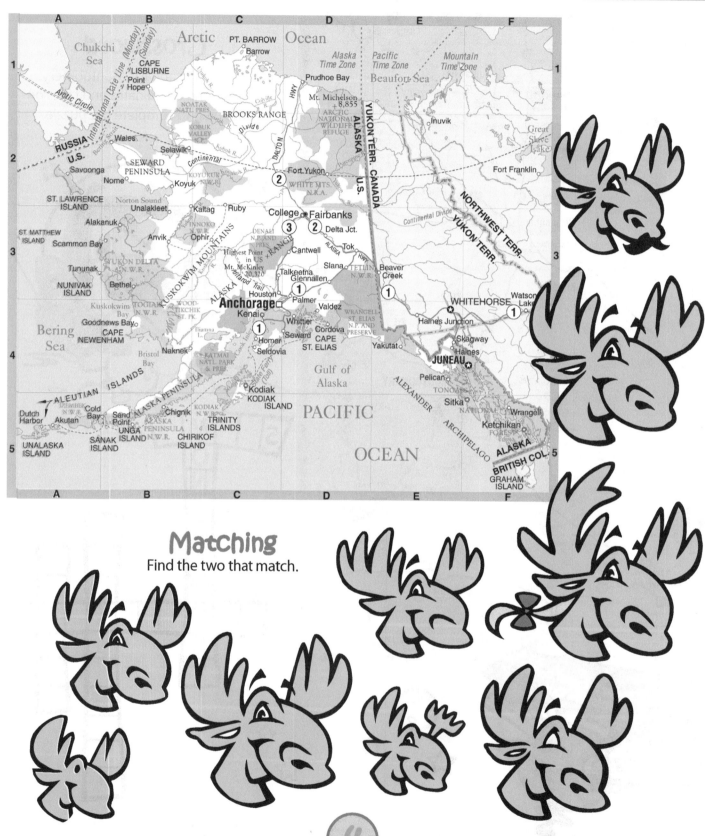

Matching
Find the two that match.

Capital City: Juneau
State Bird: Willow Ptarmigan
State Tree: Sitka Spruce
Statehood: 1959
State Flower: Forget-Me-Not

Arizona
Grand Canyon State

Color By Number

1= Red
2= Green
3= Brown
4= Yellow
5= Blue
6= Gray

5

Arkansas

The Natural State, The Razorback State

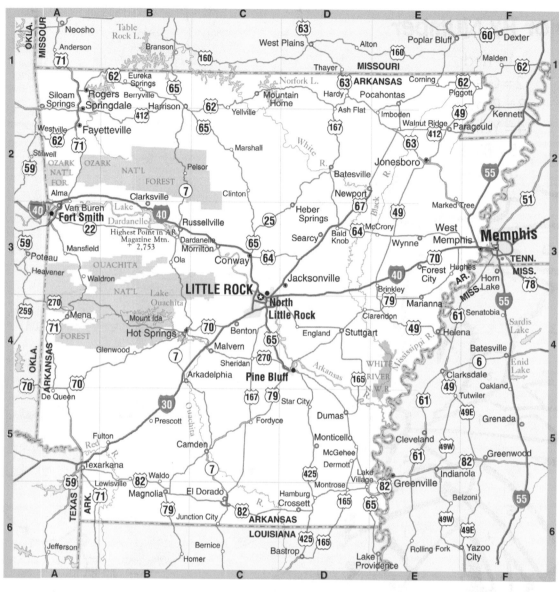

Decoder Puzzle

Decode the puzzle to name this national park in Arkansas.

| 3 | 1 | 6 | | 5 | 8 | 2 | 4 | 7 | 9 | 5 |

1 = O   3 = H   5 = S   7 = N   9 = G

2 = R   4 = I   6 = T   8 = P

Capital City: Little Rock
State Bird: Mockingbird

State Tree: Pine

6

Statehood: 1836
State Flower: Apple Blossom

California
Golden State

Art Project
Design a t-shirt featuring all the fun things there are to do in California.

Capital City: Sacramento
State Bird: California Valley Quail
State Tree: California Redwood
Statehood: 1850
State Flower: Golden Poppy

Colorado

Centennial State

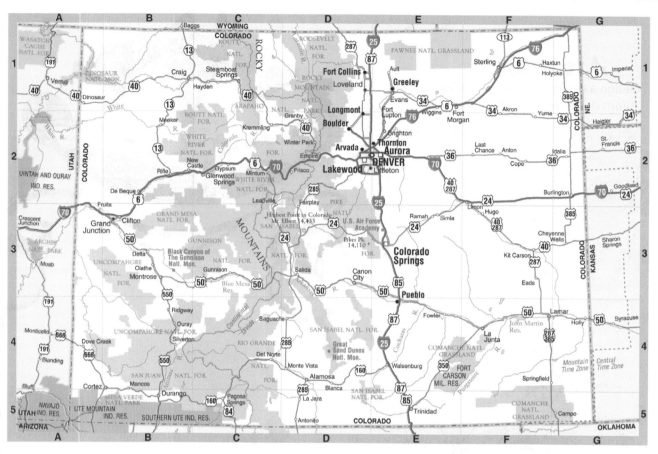

Puzzle In The Round

Start at W and write every other letter to name Colorado's neighboring states.

1. _____
2. _____
3. _____
4. _____
5. _____
6. _____
7. _____

8

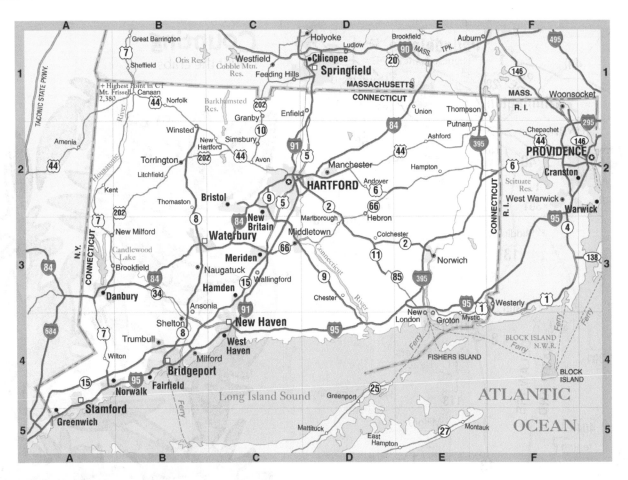

Word Smith

How many words can you make from the letters in CONNECTICUT?

_____   _____

_____   _____

_____   _____

_____   _____

Capital City: Hartford
State Bird: American Robin

State Tree: White Oak

9

Statehood: 1788
State Flower: Mountain Laurel

Delaware

First State, Diamond State

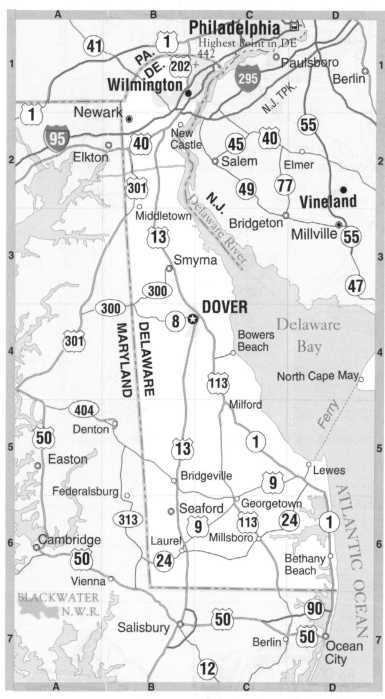

Counting
Count the crabs.

Write your answer here.

Capital City: Dover
State Bird: Blue Hen Chicken
State Tree: American Holly
Statehood: 1787
State Flower: Peach Blossom

Florida
Sunshine State

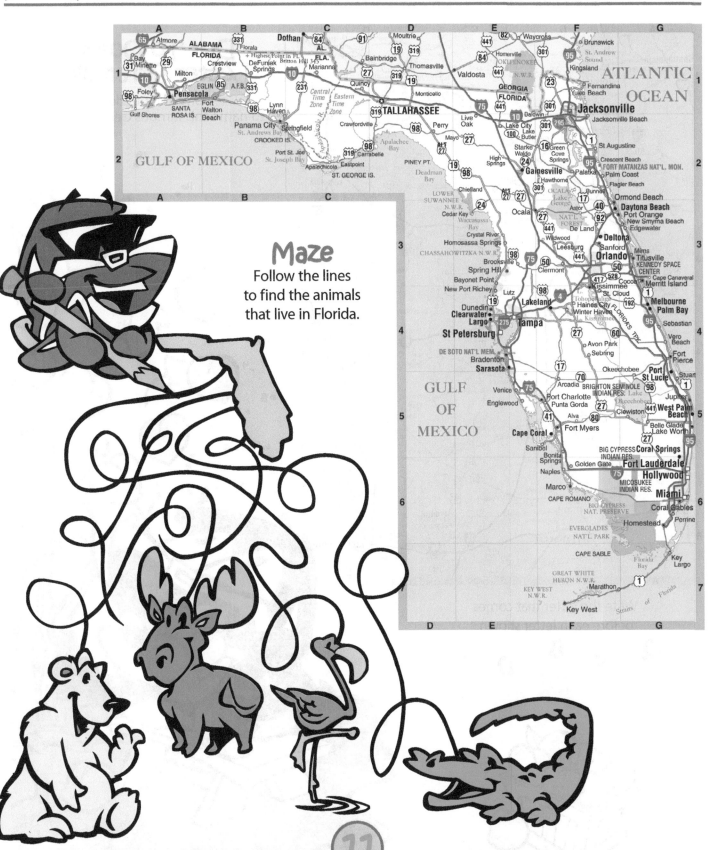

Maze
Follow the lines
to find the animals
that live in Florida.

Capital City: Tallahassee
State Bird: Mockingbird
State Tree: Sabal Palmetto Palm
Statehood: 1845
State Flower: Orange Blossom

Georgia

Empire State of the South, Peach State

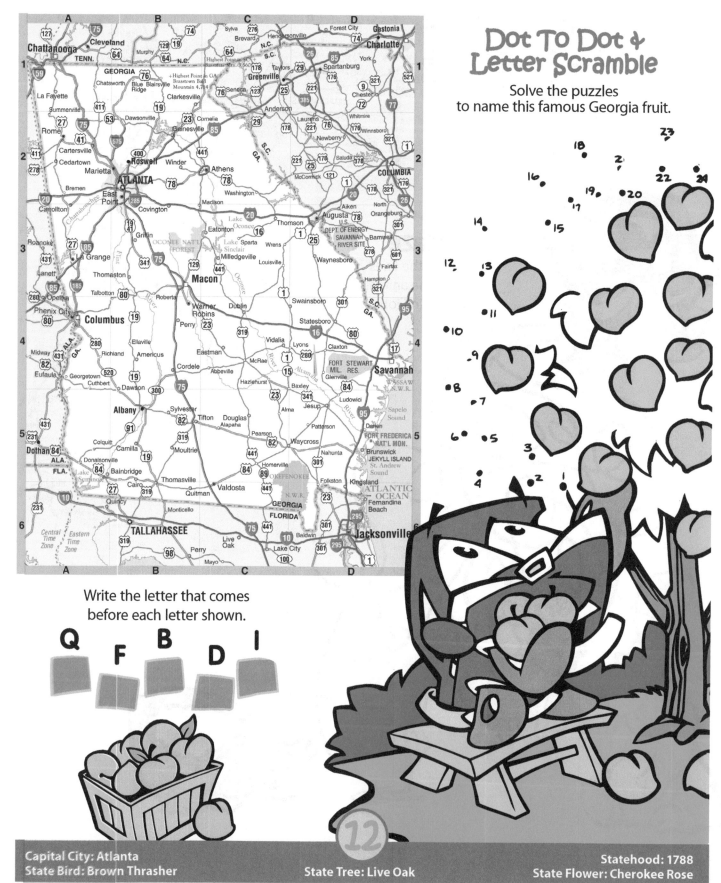

Dot To Dot & Letter Scramble

Solve the puzzles
to name this famous Georgia fruit.

Write the letter that comes
before each letter shown.

Q   F   B   D   I

Capital City: Atlanta
State Bird: Brown Thrasher
State Tree: Live Oak
Statehood: 1788
State Flower: Cherokee Rose

Hawaii
Aloha State

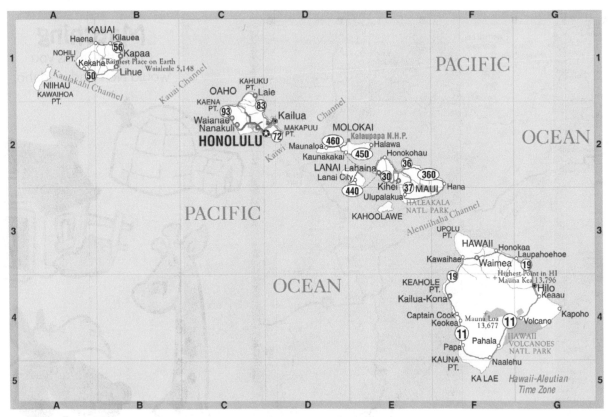

	A	B	C	D	E	F	G

1
KAUAI
Haena Kilauea
NOHILI PT. 56 Kapaa
Kekaha Rainiest Place on Earth
50 Lihue Waialeale 5,148
NIIHAU
KAWAIHOA PT.
Kaulakahi Channel
Kauai Channel

PACIFIC

2
KAHUKU PT. Laie
OAHO
KAENA PT. 93 83
Waianae Kailua
Nanakuli MAKAPUU PT.
HONOLULU 72
Kaiwi Channel
Maunaloa 460 Kalaupapa N.H.P.
MOLOKAI
Kaunakakai 450 Halawa
Honokohau
LANAI Lahaina 36
Lanai City 30 360
440 Kihei 37 MAUI Hana
Ulupalakua HALEAKALA NATL. PARK
KAHOOLAWE
Alenuihaha Channel

OCEAN

3
PACIFIC
UPOLU PT.
HAWAII Honokaa Laupahoehoe
Kawaihae Waimea 19
KEAHOLE PT. 19 Highest Point in HI
Kailua-Kona + Mauna Kea 13,796 Hilo
Keaau

OCEAN

4
Captain Cook Mauna Loa 13,677 11 Volcano Kapoho
Keokea 11 Pahala HAWAII VOLCANOES NATL. PARK
Papa KAUNA PT. Naalehu
KA LAE Hawaii-Aleutian Time Zone

5

	A	B	C	D	E	F	G

Memory Game
Look at the page for 30 seconds.

Turn to page 57 to list all the things you remember.

(13)

Capital City: Honolulu
State Bird: Hawaiian Goose
State Tree: Kukui (Candlenut)
Statehood: 1959
State Flower: Yellow Hibiscus

Idaho

Gem State

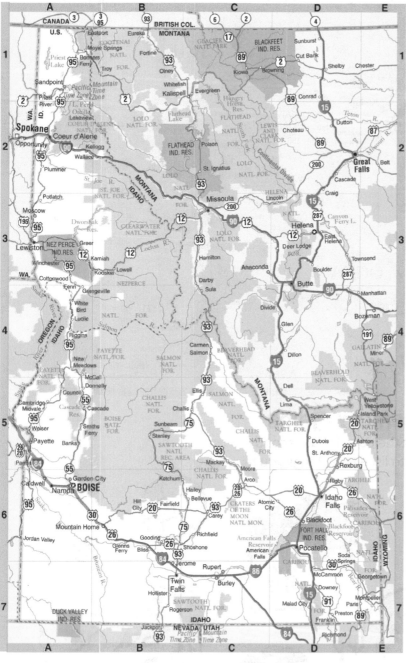

Matching

Circle the items you would NOT find in Idaho.

Capital City: Boise
State Bird: Mountain Bluebird

State Tree: White Pine

Statehood: 1890
State Flower: Syringa

Mapping Skills

Use the index on page 58 to fill in the grid coordinates for these cities.

GRID COORDINATE

Champaign _____

Chicago _____

Decatur _____

Paris _____

Rock Falls _____

Springfield _____

Waterloo _____

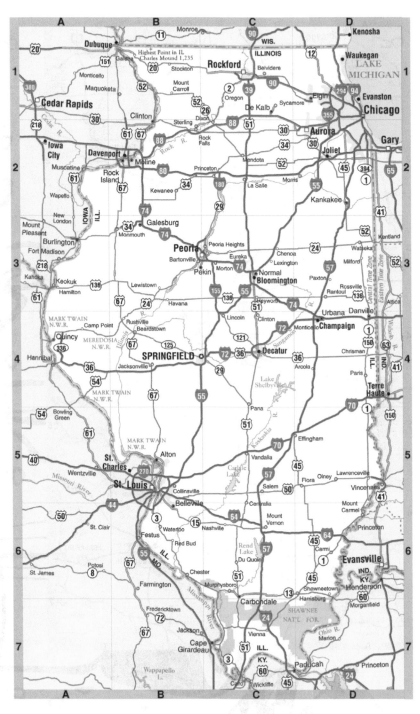

Capital City: Springfield
State Bird: Cardinal
State Tree: White Oak
Statehood: 1818
State Flower: Native Violet

Indiana

Hoosier State

Coloring

Indianapolis is the home of the Indy 500.
Color Sparky's race car with your favorite colors.

Capital City: Indianapolis
State Bird: Cardinal

State Tree: Tulip Poplar

Statehood: 1816
State Flower: Peony

Iowa
Hawkeye State

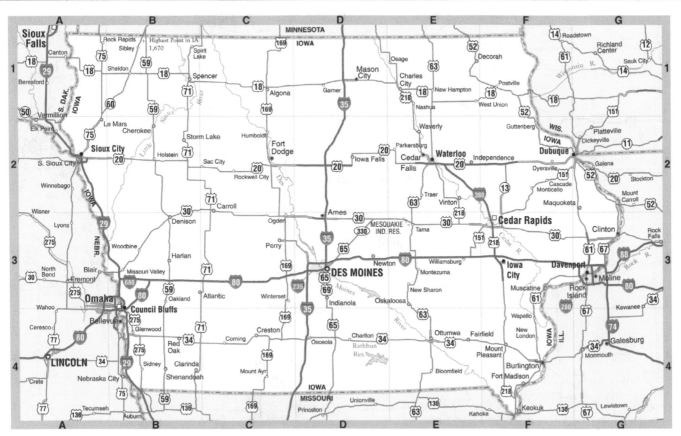

What's Wrong With This Picture?
Circle all the things wrong with this picture.

17

Kansas

Sunflower State

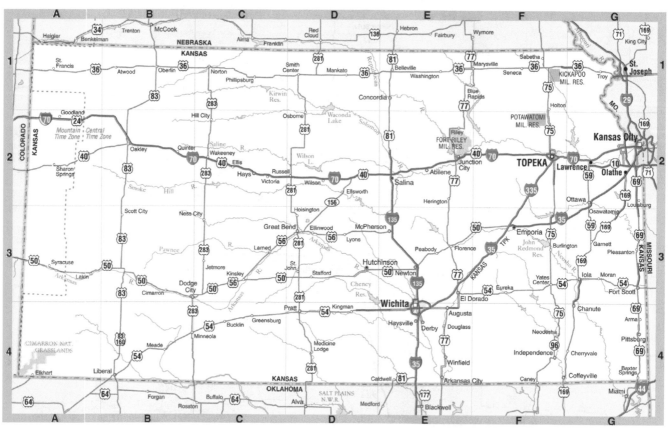

Word Scramble

Cross out all of the X's, Z's and O's to spell the name

XZXWZXYOXOAOXXOTZOZTX

XZEOXAORZXXPOZ

Capital City: Topeka
State Bird: Western Meadowlark
State Tree: Cottonwood
Statehood: 1861
State Flower: Native Sunflower

Kentucky
Bluegrass State

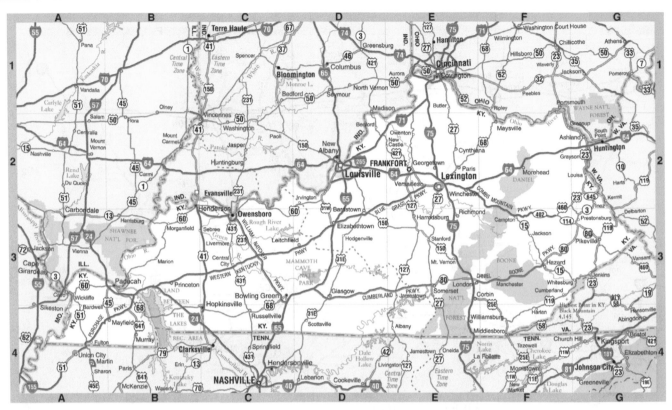

Decoder Puzzle

Write the first letter of each item to name this famous Kentucky frontiersman.

19

Louisiana

Pelican State

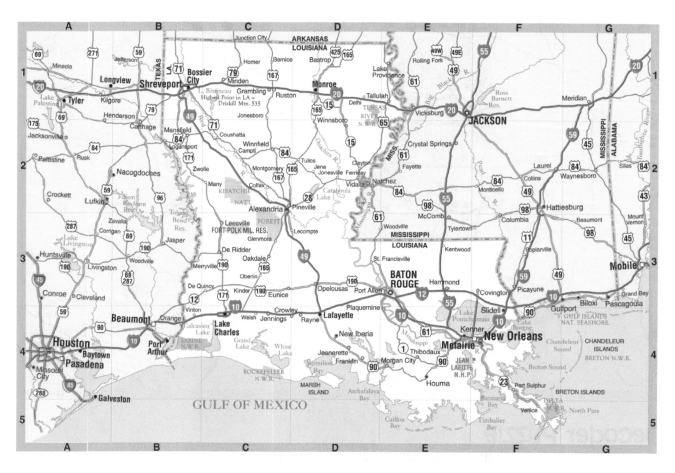

Word Search

Jean Lafitte was a famous pirate. How many times does the word "PIRATE" appear?

Remember, the words can appear forwards, backwards, up, down, and diagonally.

```
P G D F E K P I R A T E
I E B X R Y Y G F M P F
R G F J D E T A R I P F
A H C R G C N U R F Y D
T P F F T A B E R V J H
E H P I R A T E D D I Y
H T H F D A F K C E L E
U M J D R T D O G S O T
K L T I P I R A T E U A
A Y P E T N Z L J S J R
Q E G S G G A Y K Q G I
E T A R I P A R I P H P
```

Capital City: Baton Rouge
State Bird: Eastern Brown Pelican
State Tree: Cypress
Statehood: 1812
State Flower: Magnolia

Maine
Pine Tree State

Maze
Help Sparky get through the maze.

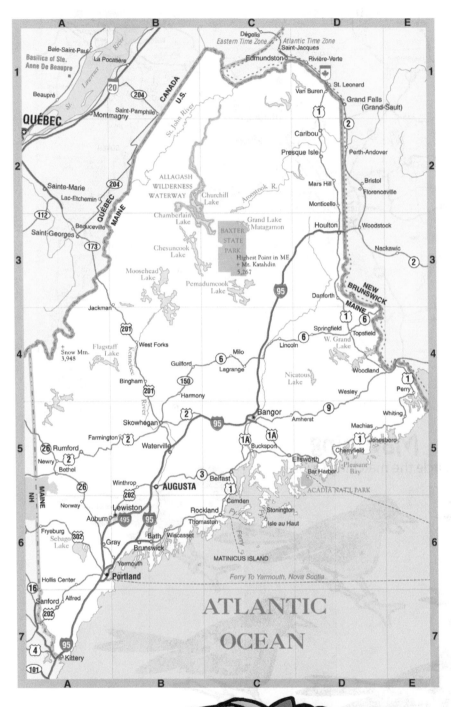

Capital City: Augusta
State Bird: Chickadee
State Tree: Eastern White Pine
Statehood: 1820
State Flower: White Pine Cone & Tassel

Maryland

Old Line State, Free State

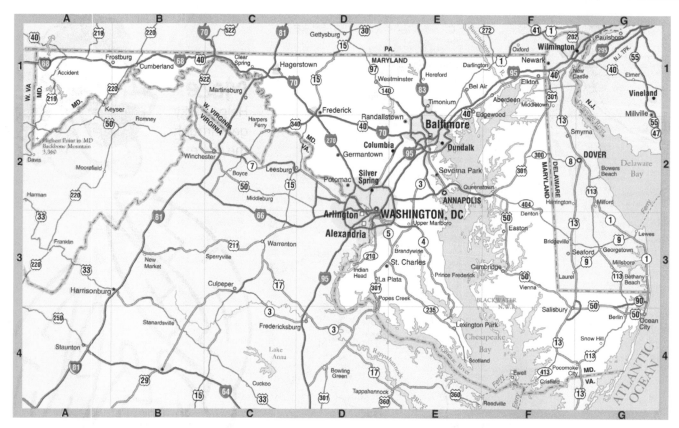

Matching

Circle the matching Orioles.

Capital City: Annapolis
State Bird: Baltimore Oriole

State Tree: White Oak

Statehood: 1788
State Flower: Black Eyed Susan

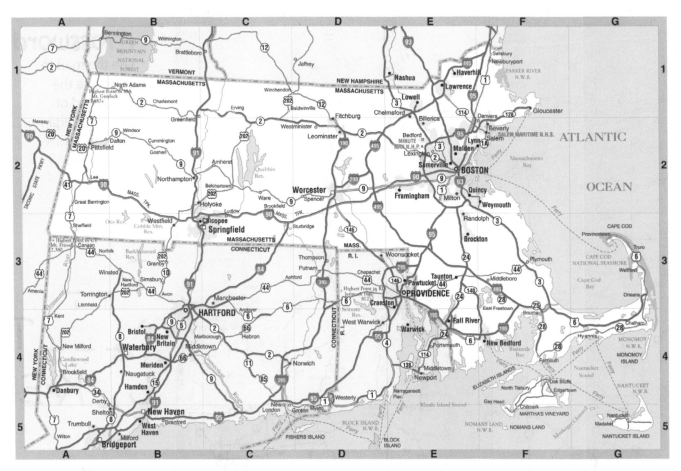

Word Smith

How many words can you make from the letters in MASSACHUSETTS?

_____   _____
_____   _____
_____   _____
_____   _____
_____   _____
_____   _____
_____   _____
_____   _____

23

Michigan

Great Lakes State

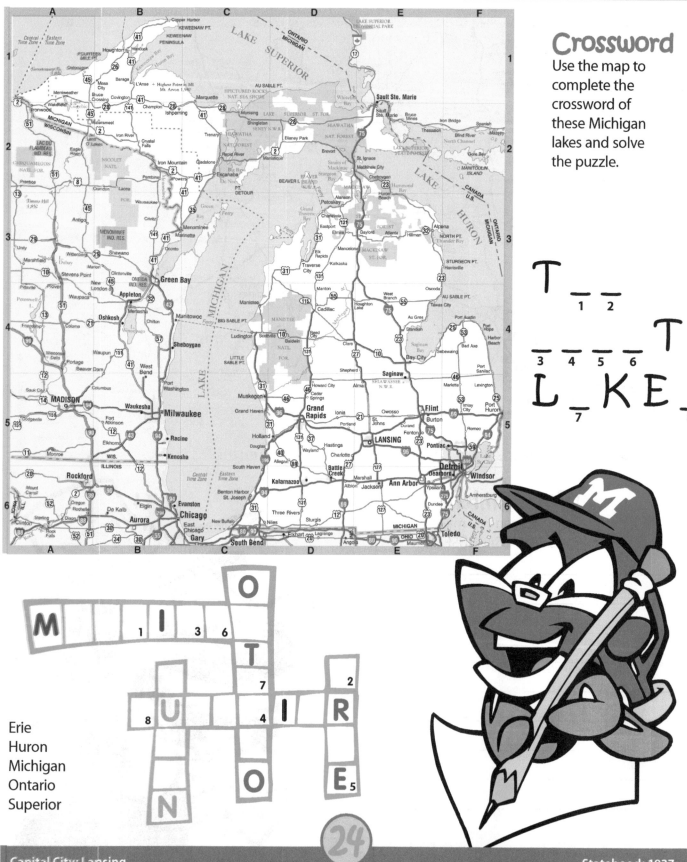

Crossword

Use the map to complete the crossword of these Michigan lakes and solve the puzzle.

T _ _ _ _ T
(1)(2)
(3)(4)(5)(6)
L _ K E _
(7)(8)

Erie
Huron
Michigan
Ontario
Superior

Minnesota

North Star State, Gopher State

City Scramble

Unscramble the letters
to name these
Minnesota cities.

TS. OUDLC [B-4]

__ __ • __ __ __ __ __

DRE • GWIN [D-5]

__ __ __ • __ __ __ __

OANSCKJ [B-6]

__ __ __ __ __ __ __

OOKC [C-2]

__ __ __ __

UULDHT [D-3]

__ __ __ __ __ __

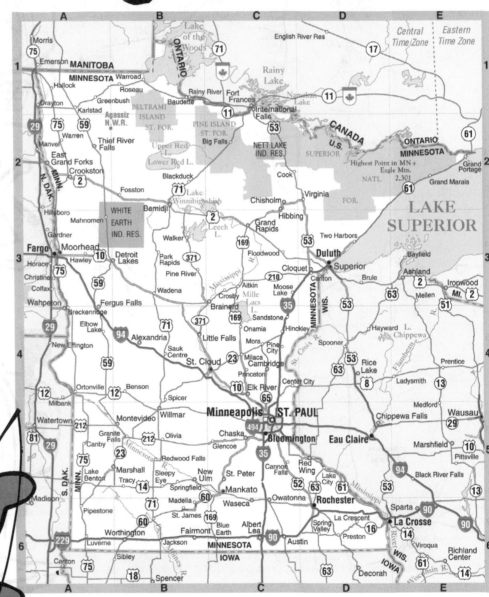

Capital City: St. Paul
State Bird: Common Loon

State Tree: Red Pine

Statehood: 1858
State Flower: Pink & White Lady's Slipper

Matching

In honor of Mississippi, the Magnolia state,
circle all the items that begin with the letter "M".

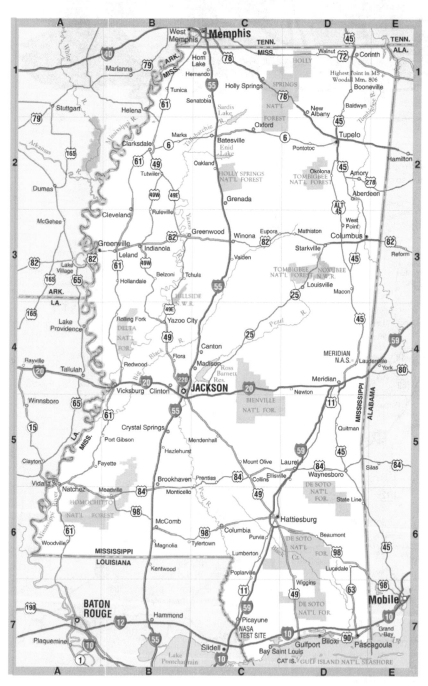

26

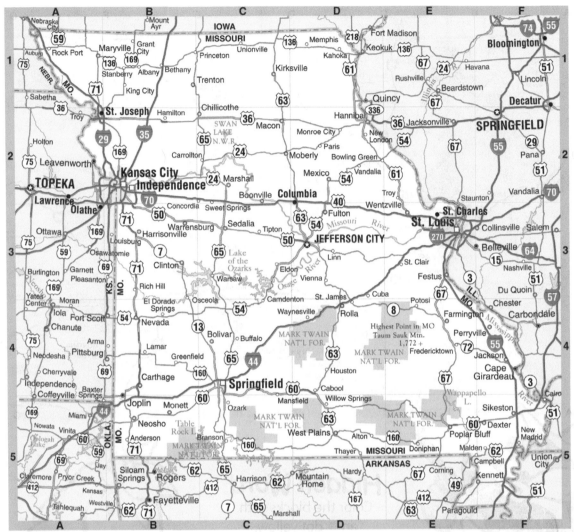

Mapping

Use the map to complete the sentences.

1. Springfield is _____ of Joplin.

   East   South   West

2. Columbia is on U.S. _____.

   70   40   35

3. The capital city is marked with a _____.

   Star   triangle   X

4. St. Louis is near the _____ state border.

   Arkansas   Kansas   Illinois

27

Montana

Treasure State

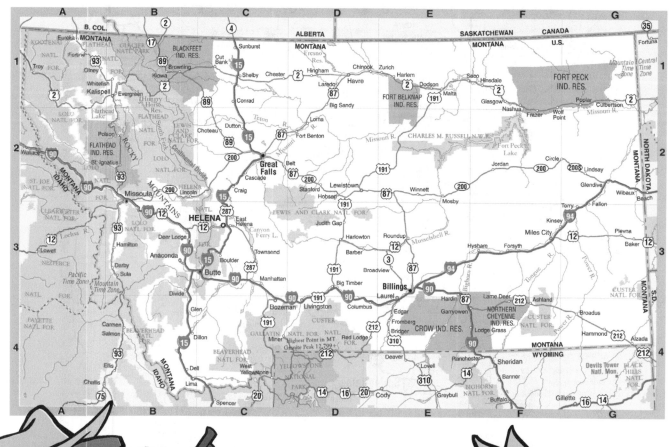

Hidden Word

Color the blocks with
an ● dot yellow.
Color the blocks with
a ● dot black
to reveal the hidden word.

Capital City: Helena
State Bird: Western Meadowlark
State Tree: Ponderosa Pine
Statehood: 1889
State Flower: Bitterroot

Nebraska
Cornhusker State

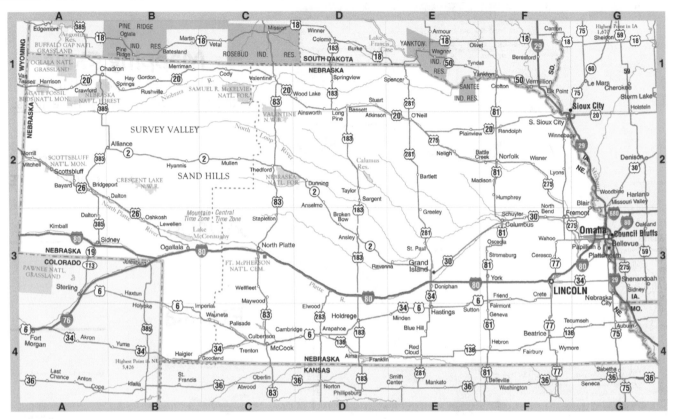

Maze
Help Sparky find his way through the maze.

29

Capital City: Lincoln
State Bird: Western Meadowlark
State Tree: Cottonwood
Statehood: 1867
State Flower: Goldenrod

Nevada

Sagebrush State, Silver State

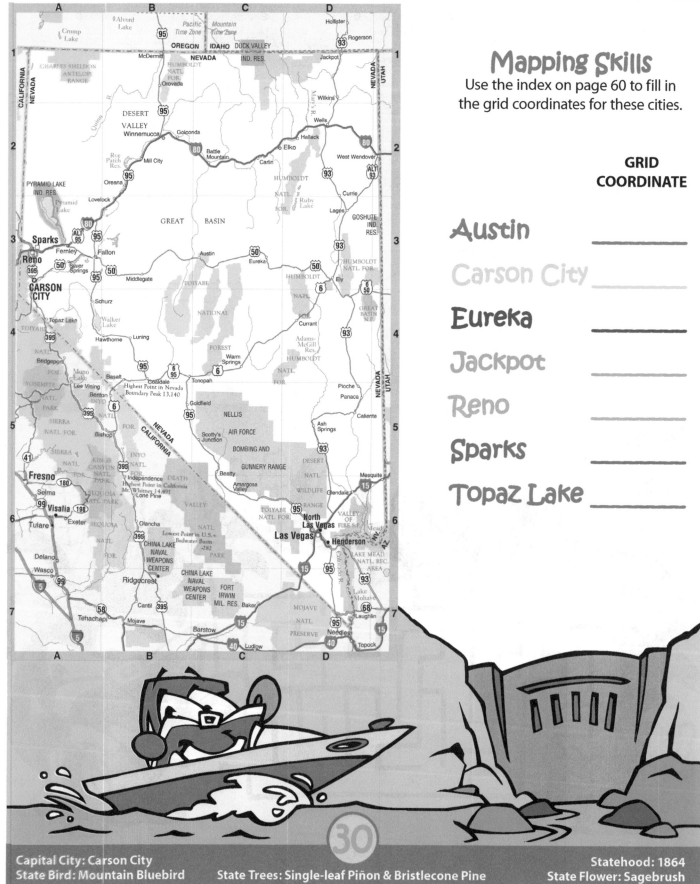

Use the index on page 60 to fill in the grid coordinates for these cities.

Mapping Skills

	GRID COORDINATE
Austin	
Carson City	
Eureka	
Jackpot	
Reno	
Sparks	
Topaz Lake	

30

Capital City: Carson City
State Bird: Mountain Bluebird
State Trees: Single-leaf Piñon & Bristlecone Pine
Statehood: 1864
State Flower: Sagebrush

New Hampshire

Granite State

	State	Animal
Lancaster	louisiana	
Concord		
Portsmouth		puma
Manchester		
Nashua		

Alphabet Soup
Using the first letter of the city, fill in the boxes. No word or name can be used more than once.

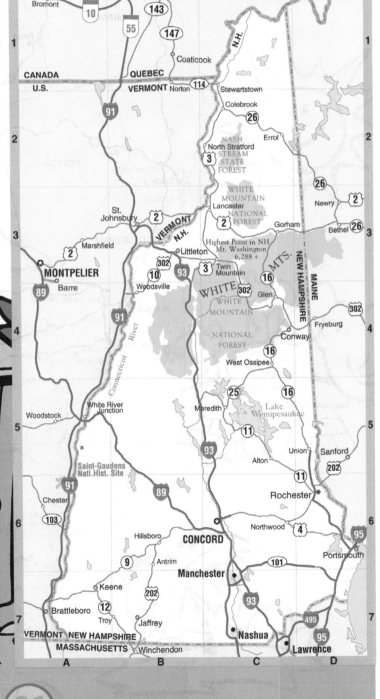

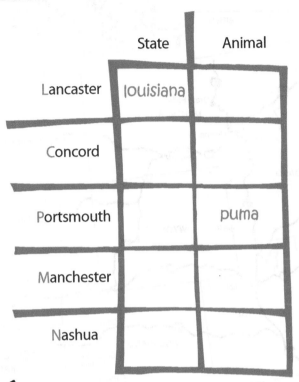

Capital City: Concord
State Bird: Purple Finch

State Tree: White Birch

Statehood: 1788
State Flower: Purple Lilac

U.S.A.

Coloring

Use your favorite colors to color the sights you might see as you travel across the U.S.A.

ZOO

BRITISH COLUMBIA

ALBERTA

SASKATCHEWAN
Regina

MANITOBA
Winnipeg

Seattle
Olympia
WASHINGTON
5
90
Spokane
82
Pasco
Portland
84
Salem
5
OREGON

15
Great Falls
MONTANA
90
Butte
Helena
Billings
90
Boise
IDAHO
84
Pocatello
15

NORTH DAKOTA
Grand Forks
94
Bismarck
Fargo

SOUTH DAKOTA
Rapid City
90
Sioux Falls

WYOMING
90
Casper
25

Reno
80
NEVADA
80
Salt Lake City
Cheyenne
NEBRASKA
80
Om
Lincol

Sacramento
Oakland
San Francisco
5
UTAH
Denver
70
COLORADO
Colorado Springs
Pueblo
70
KANSAS
135
Wichita

CALIFORNIA
5
15
Las Vegas
25

San Bernardino
40
ARIZONA
Santa Fe
Los Angeles
10
40
Albuquerque
40
Amarillo
Oklahoma City
OKLAHOMA
35

San Diego
Mexicali
8
17
Phoenix
NEW MEXICO
25
Lubbock
Ft. Worth
20

Tucson
10
El Paso
10
TEXAS
35

Austin
H
10

Barrow
San Antonio
35
37

Nome
Fairbanks
YUKON TERRITORY
MEXICO
Nuevo Laredo

Bethel
ALASKA
Anchorage
Juneau
Monterrey
Matamoros

Kodiak
HAWAII
Ciudad Victoria

Aleutian Islands
Honolulu
Hilo

32

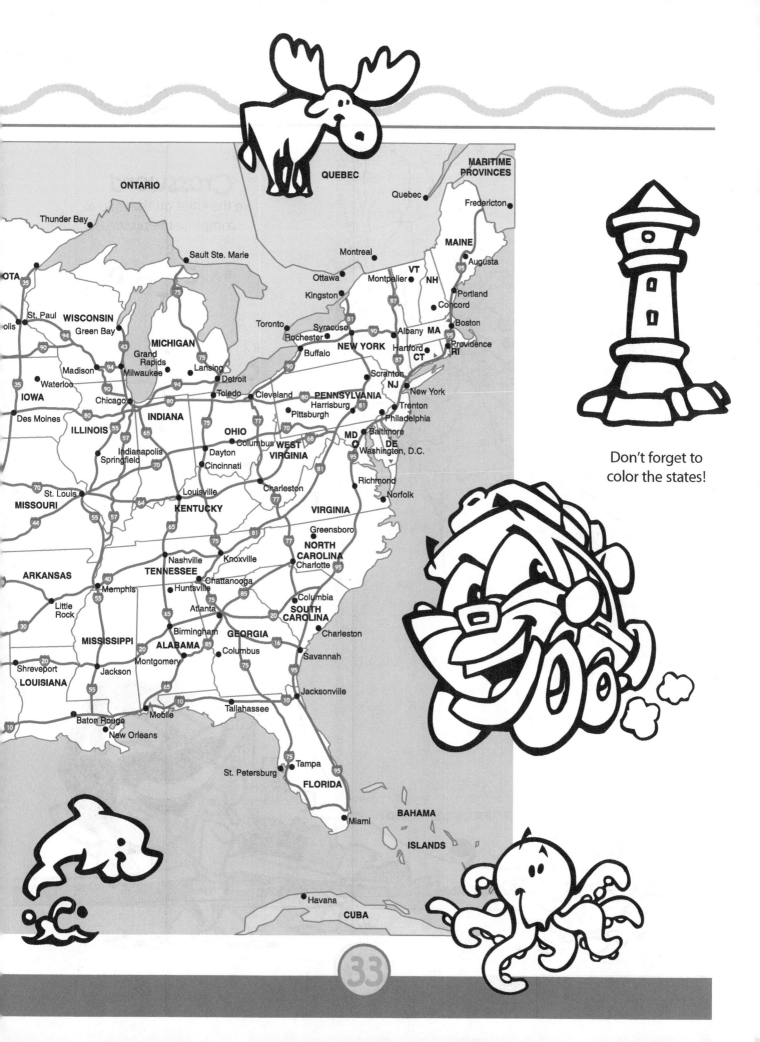

Don't forget to color the states!

New Jersey

Garden State

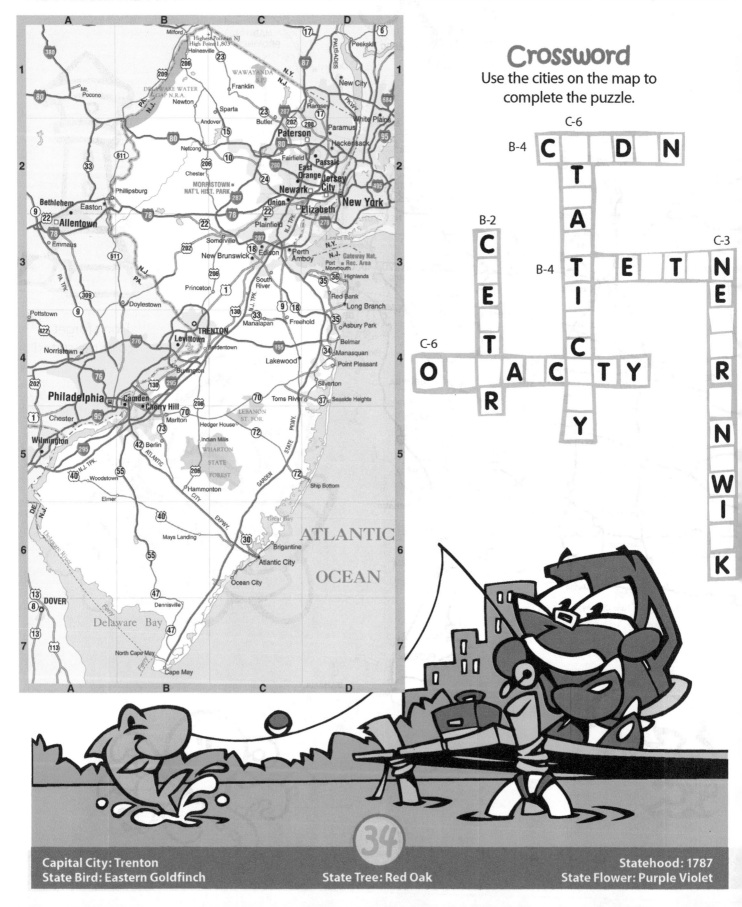

Crossword

Use the cities on the map to complete the puzzle.

C-6
B-4 **C** **D** **N**

B-2 **C**

B-4 **E** **T**

C-3 **N**

C-6 **O** **A** **C** **T** **Y**

Capital City: Trenton
State Bird: Eastern Goldfinch
State Tree: Red Oak
Statehood: 1787
State Flower: Purple Violet

```
A  O  S  N  N  P  F  T  E
E  H  W  E  I  T  A  S  G
E  A  E  F  N  I  R  E  S
U  H  T  A  U  C  M  Q  P
Q  A  L  T  S  R  I  Z  L
R  S  L  N  S  B  N  U  M
E  A  Q  A  N  R  G  F  J
U  L  T  S  B  B  T  H  T
Q  O  B  B  L  S  O  H  E
U  A  R  O  W  B  N  G  T
B  L  R  E  B  E  E  J  E  S
L  R  O  S  W  E  L  L  S
A  L  A  M  A  Z  T  E  C
```

Word Search
Find and circle these New Mexico cities.

Word Bank
Albuquerque • Aztec • Farmington
Hobbs • Roswell • Santa Fe

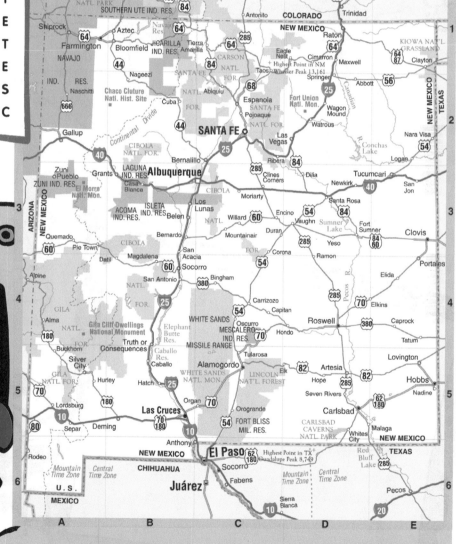

Capital City: Santa Fe
State Bird: Roadrunner

State Tree: Piñon

Statehood: 1912
State Flower: Yucca

New York

Empire State

Art Project
Design a postcard for New York City.

Capital City: Albany
State Bird: Bluebird

State Tree: Sugar Maple

Statehood: 1788
State Flower: Rose

North Carolina

Tar Heel State, Old North State

Mystery Place

Circle all of the letters, except for X's, Z's and O's
to spell the site of the Wright Brothers' first airplane flight.

XKOIXZTXTXOYZ · OHXXZAOXWZOKO

_____ _____ _____ _____ _____ · _____ _____ _____ _____

Capital City: Raleigh
State Bird: Cardinal

State Tree: Pine

Statehood: 1789
State Flower: Dogwood

North Dakota

Peace Garden State

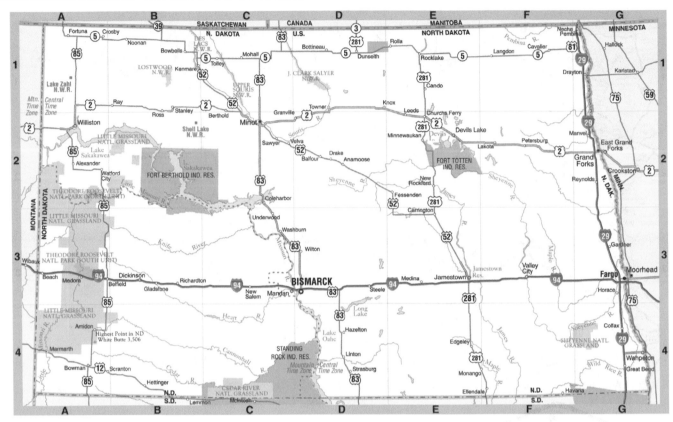

Coloring

North Dakota is the #1 producer of sunflower seeds in the U.S.
Sunflowers come in a variety of colors. Color the page with your favorites!

38

Capital City: Bismarck
State Bird: Western Meadowlark
State Tree: American Elm
Statehood: 1889
State Flower: Wild Prairie Rose

Scramble

To name this Ohio favorite past time cross out all the capital letters. Write the remaining letters in the spaces.

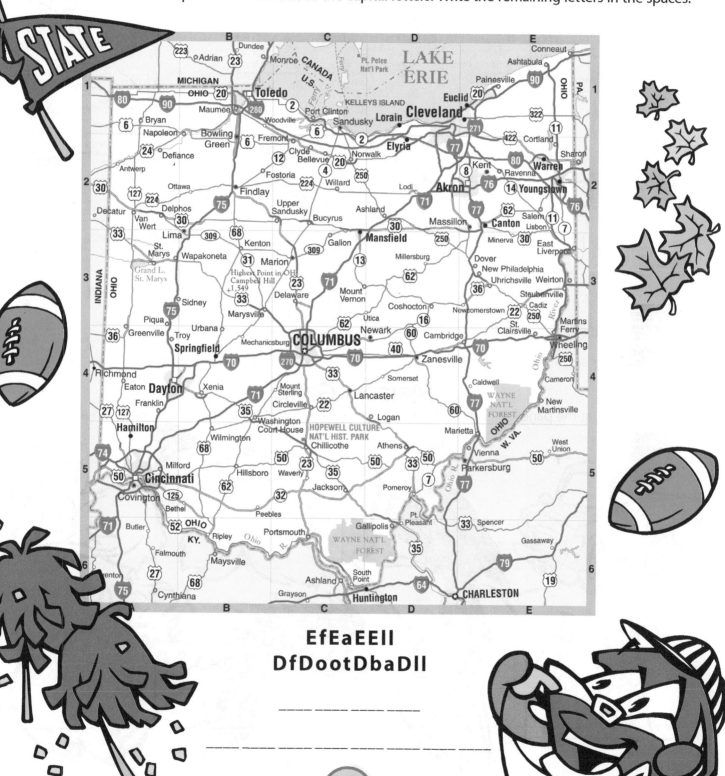

EfEaEEll

DfDootDbaDll

____ ____ ____ ____

____ ____ ____ ____ ____ ____ ____

Capital City: Columbus
State Bird: Cardinal
State Tree: Buckeye
Statehood: 1803
State Flower: Scarlet Carnation

Oklahoma

Sooner State

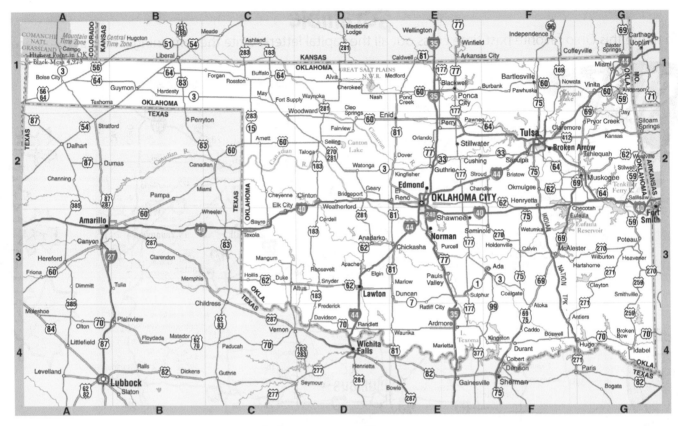

Memory Game

Look at the page for 15 seconds. Turn to page 57 to list all the items you can remember.

Capital City: Oklahoma City
State Bird: Scissor-tailed Flycatcher
State Tree: Redbud
Statehood: 1907
State Flower: Mistletoe

Oregon

Beaver State

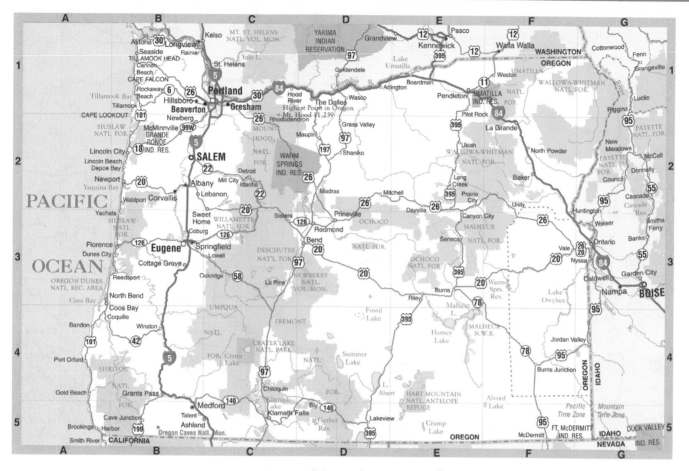

What Is Wrong With This Picture?

Look at this picture closely. Can you find the 10 things that do not belong?

41

Capital City: Salem
State Bird: Western Meadowlark

State Tree: Douglas Fir

Statehood: 1859
State Flower: Oregon Grape

Pennsylvania

Keystone State

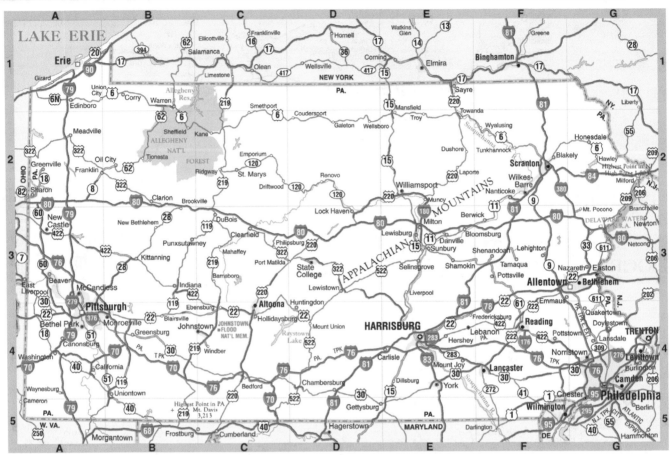

Decoding Puzzle

Decode the puzzle to name this famous Pennsylvania resident.

Capital City: Harrisburg
State Bird: Ruffed Grouse
State Tree: Hemlock
Statehood: 1787
State Flower: Mountain Laurel

Rhode Island

Little Rhody, Ocean State

Color By Number

#1= Red
#2= Yellow
#3= Purple
#4= Green
#5= Blue
#6= Gray

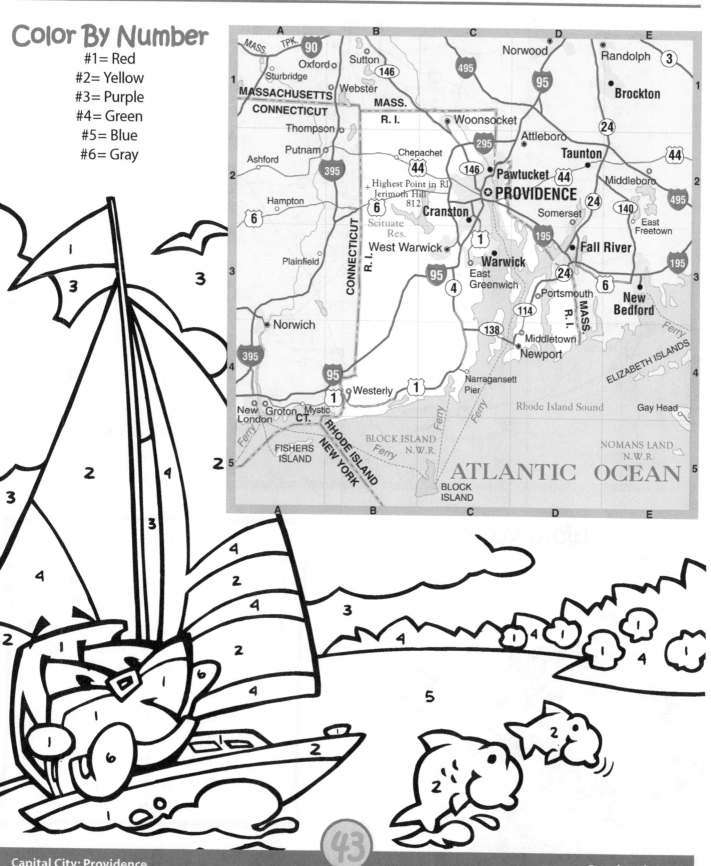

Capital City: Providence
State Bird: Rhode Island Red

State Tree: Red Maple

Statehood: 1790
State Flower: Violet

South Carolina

Palmetto State

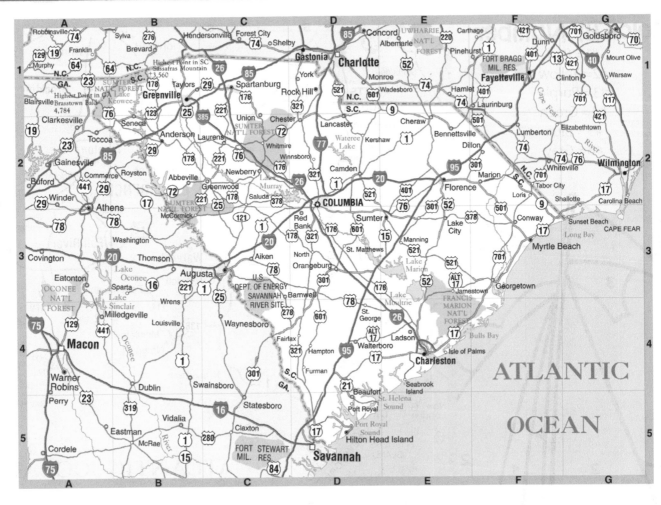

Word Search

South Carolina's other nickname is "Low Country". How many times does "Low Country" appear in this puzzle? Circle each one. It may appear forwards, backwards, up, down and diagonally.

How many did you find?

```
C  N  S  U  S  L  S  S  G  U  Y  R
E  L  W  R  I  O  Q  E  R  P  R  Y
T  O  E  A  N  W  L  Q  L  M  T  R
Z  W  Y  O  W  C  O  U  N  T  N  T
A  C  L  R  S  O  F  E  C  G  U  N
T  O  B  I  T  U  R  W  O  F  O  U
U  U  Q  N  N  N  P  O  C  L  C  O
F  N  T  G  L  T  U  L  C  F  W  C
B  T  B  Q  Q  R  R  O  O  G  O  W
S  R  U  O  M  Y  U  T  C  B  L  O
G  Y  Y  R  T  N  U  O  C  W  O  L
A  R  G  A  E  N  W  L  X  E  O  G
L  O  W  C  O  U  N  T  R  Y  D  L
```

(44)

Capital City: Columbia
State Bird: Carolina Wren

State Tree: Palmetto

Statehood: 1788
State Flower: Yellow Jessamine

South Dakota

Coyote State, Mount Rushmore State

Picture Puzzle

Decode the puzzle to name this famous monument featuring
Presidents Roosevelt, Washington, Lincoln and Jefferson.

1=U 2=R 3=M 4=O 5=E 6=S 7=N 8=H 9=T

3 4 1 7 9

2 1 6 8 3 4 2 5

Capital City: Pierre
State Bird: Chinese Ring Necked Pheasant   **State Tree: Black Hills Spruce**

Statehood: 1889
State Flower: Pasqueflower

Tennessee

Volunteer State

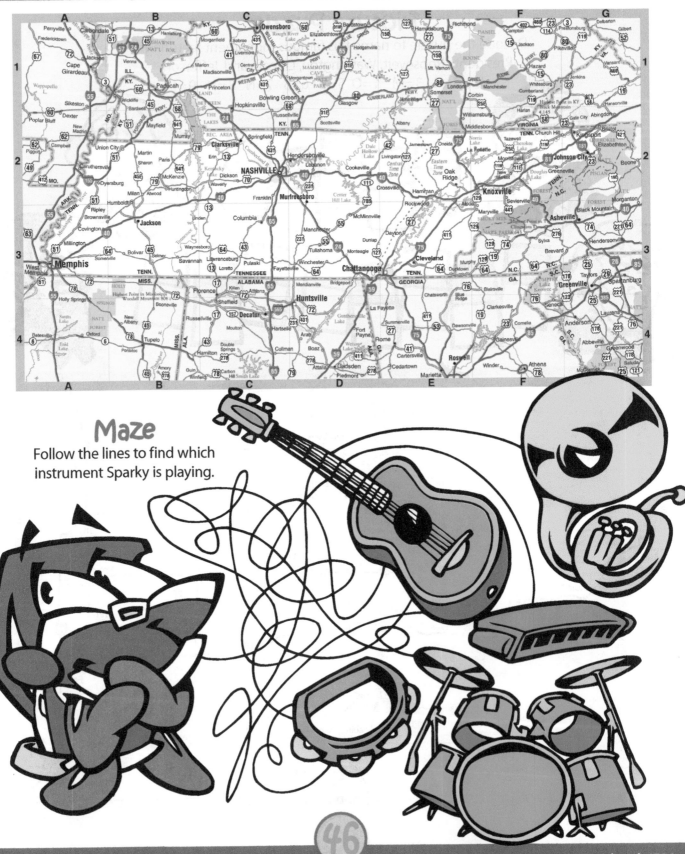

Maze
Follow the lines to find which instrument Sparky is playing.

46

Capital City: Nashville
State Bird: Mockingbird
State Tree: Tulip Poplar
Statehood: 1796
State Flower: Iris

Texas

Lone Star State

Coloring

Color the animals you would NOT find on a Texas ranch.

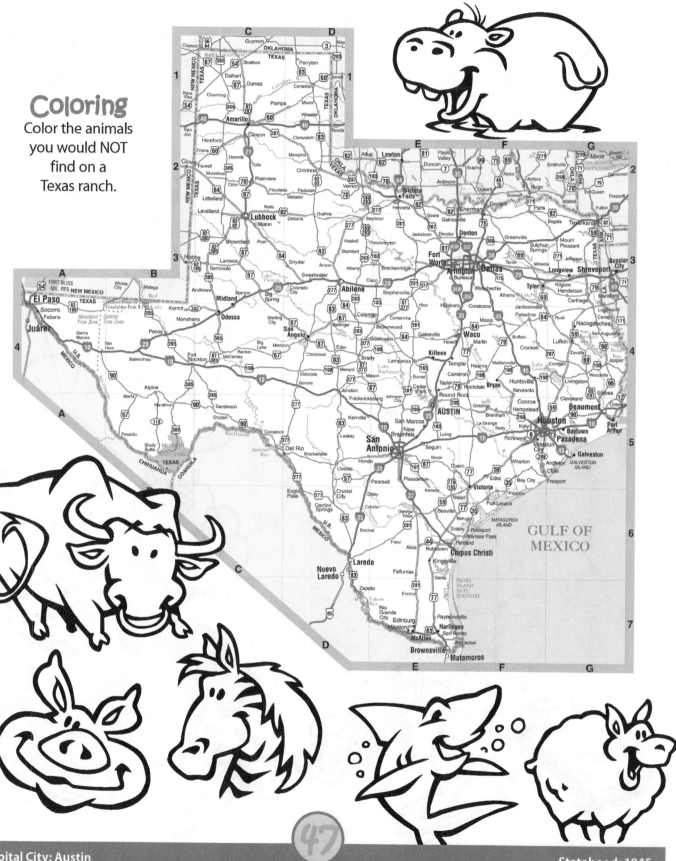

GULF OF MEXICO

Capital City: Austin
State Bird: Mockingbird

State Tree: Pecan

Statehood: 1845
State Flower: Bluebonnet

Utah

Beehive State

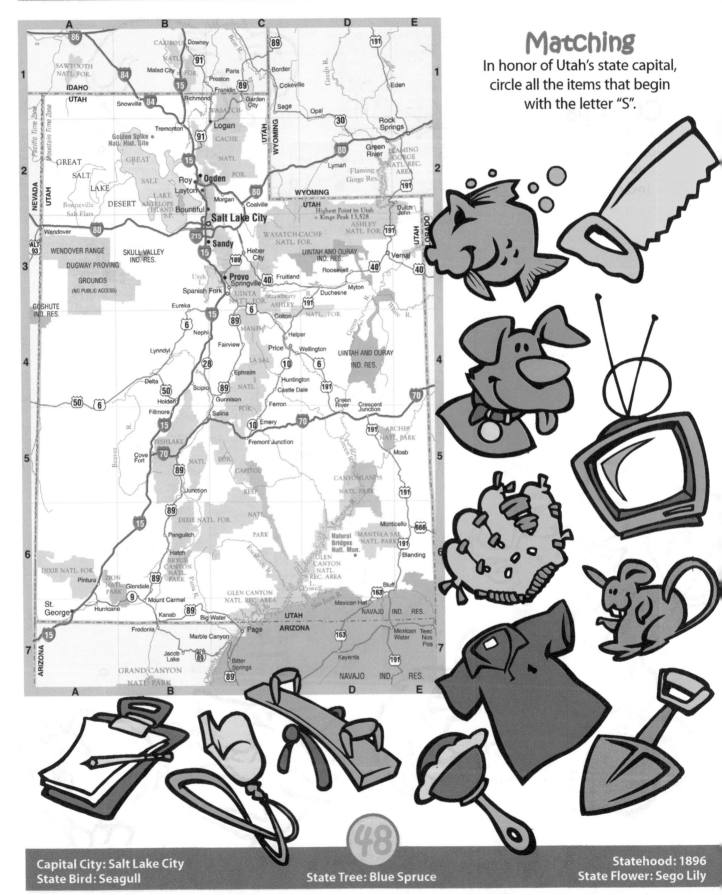

Matching

In honor of Utah's state capital, circle all the items that begin with the letter "S".

Capital City: Salt Lake City
State Bird: Seagull

State Tree: Blue Spruce

Statehood: 1896
State Flower: Sego Lily

Vermont

Green Mountain State

Color By Number

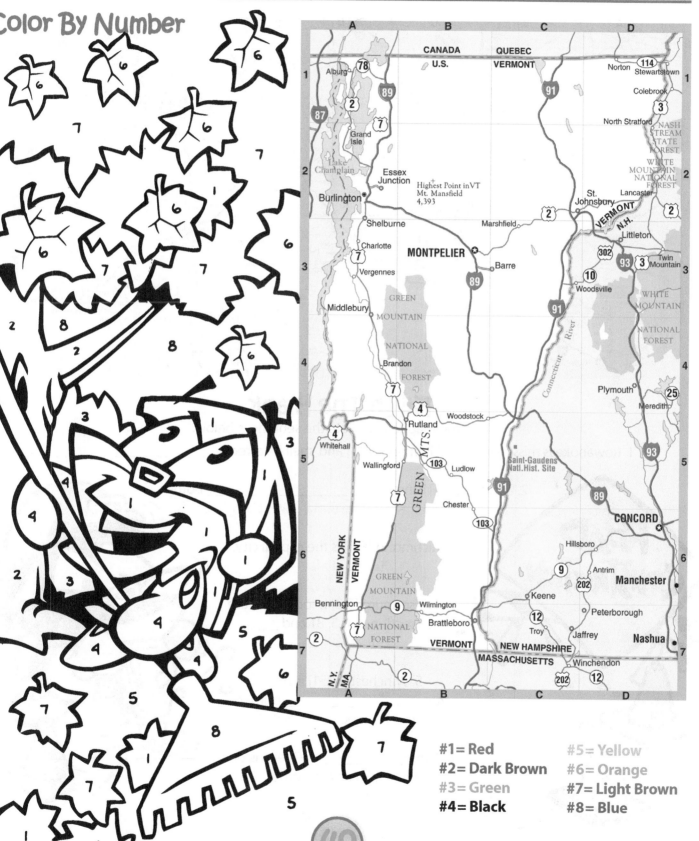

#1= **Red**　　　#5= Yellow

#2= **Dark Brown**　#6= **Orange**

#3= Green　　　#7= **Light Brown**

#4= **Black**　　#8= **Blue**

49

Capital City: Montpelier
State Bird: Hermit Thrush
State Tree: Sugar Maple
Statehood: 1791
State Flower: Red Clover

Virginia

Old Dominion

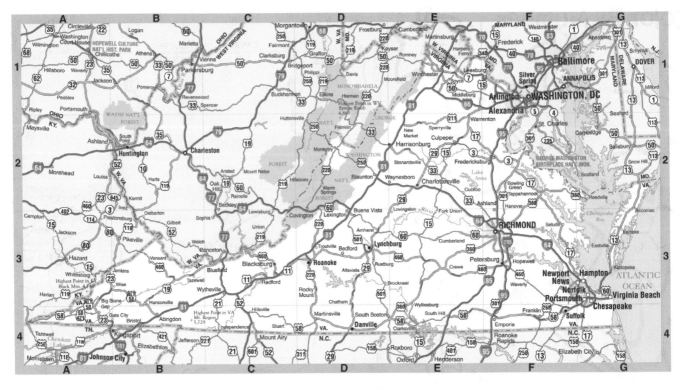

Fill In The Blank

Use the map to complete the sentences below.

1. Rowanoke is misspelled. Find it in grid [D-3] and spell it correctly. _____

2. Danville [D-4] is near the _____ border.

   Maryland   North Carolina   West Virginia

3. Richmond [F-3] is the capital city.

   True or False

4. Harrisonburg [E-2] is located at the intersection of U.S. 81 and _____.

   250   33   211

5. Winchester [E-1] is near the _____ border.

   Kentucky   Tennessee   West Virginia

6. The _____ Ocean is on Virginia's eastern border.

   Pacific   Atlantic

50

Capital City: Richmond
State Bird: Cardinal

State Tree: Dogwood

Statehood: 1788
State Flower: Dogwood

Washington

Evergreen State

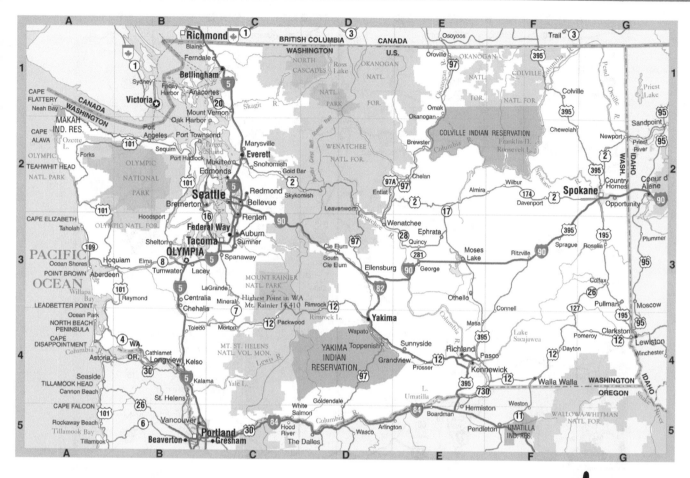

Word Scramble

Use the grid coordinates on the map to help
you unscramble these Washington cities.

1. I A A Y K M [D-4]   _____
2. E A T T S E L [B-2]   _____
3. A K N E P O S [G-2]   _____
4. T T E E V E R [C-2]   _____
5. I Y L A O P M [B-3]   _____
6. A A M O C T [C-3]   _____

51

Capital City: Olympia
State Bird: Willow Goldfinch
State Tree: Western Hemlock
Statehood: 1889
State Flower: Western Rhododendron

West Virginia

Mountain State

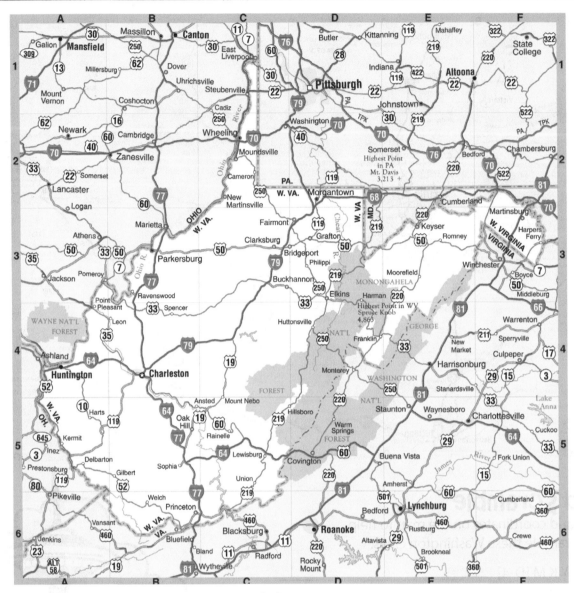

Maze

Did you know West Virginia is the #1 coal producing state in the U.S. ?

Capital City: Charleston
State Bird: Cardinal

State Tree: Sugar Maple

Statehood: 1863
State Flower: Big Rhododendron

Wisconsin

Badger State

Matching

Find the matching cheese wedges.

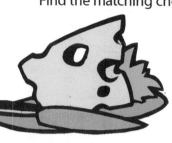

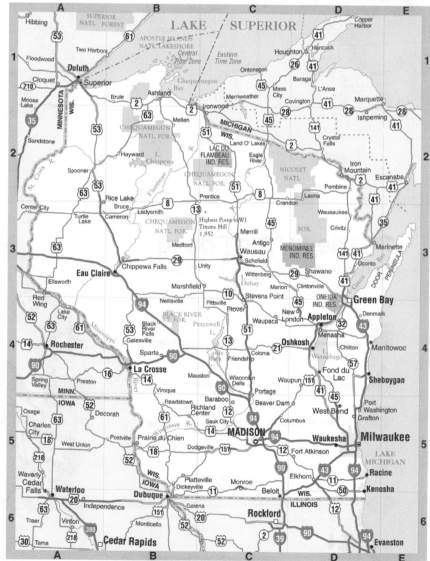

53

Capital City: Madison
State Bird: Robin

State Tree: Sugar Maple

Statehood: 1848
State Flower: Wood Violet

Wyoming

Equality State

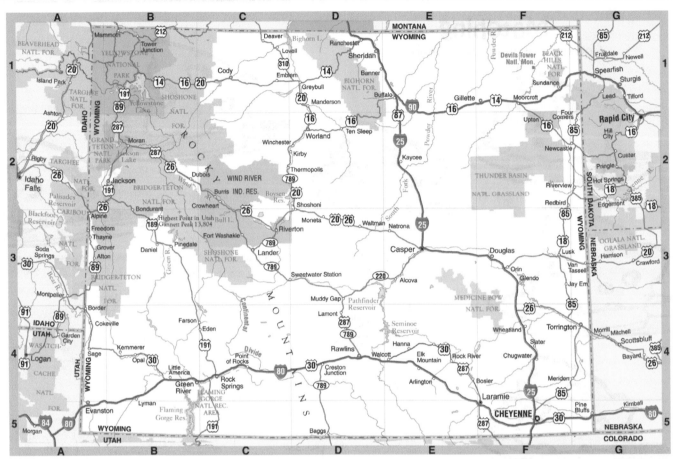

Puzzle-In-The-Round

Start at C and write every other letter to name these Wyoming cities.

1 _____

2 _____

3 _____

4 _____

5 _____

6 _____

54

Capital City: Cheyenne
State Bird: Meadowlark
State Tree: Cottonwood
Statehood: 1890
State Flower: Indian Paintbrush

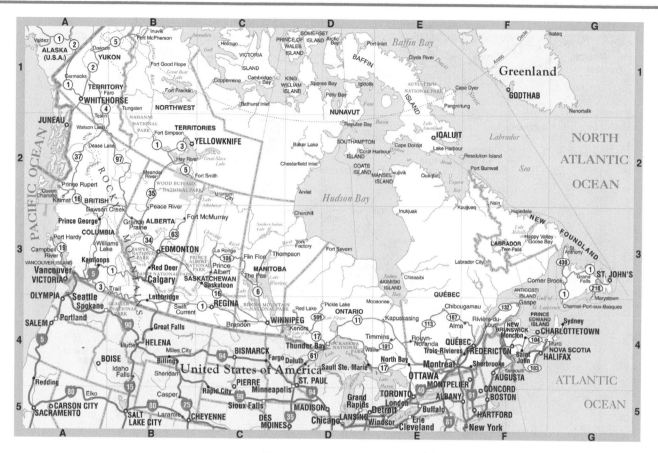

Dot To Dot

Complete the dot-to-dot to see the picture.

Mexico

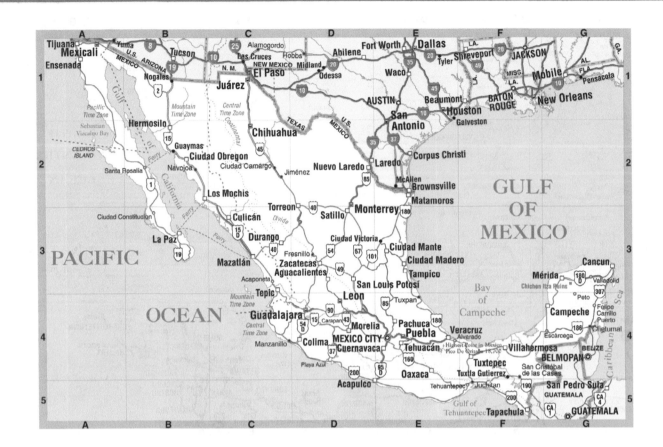

Word Smith

Using the first letter of these Mexican cities, fill in the boxes.
No word or name can be used twice.

	City Name	Boy's Name	Girl's Name
Acapulco	aguacalientes		
Monterrey			
Chihuahua			callie

MEMORY GAME

Page 13
_____
_____
_____
_____
_____
_____
_____
_____
_____
_____
_____
_____

Page 40
_____
_____
_____
_____
_____
_____
_____
_____
_____
_____
_____
_____

INDEX TO CITIES, TOWNS & PLACES

ALABAMA
ALABASTER.....B-3
ALEXANDER CITY.....D-4
ANDALUSIA.....C-6
ANNISTON.....C-3
ARAB.....C-2
ATHENS.....B-1
ATMORE.....B-6
ATTALLA.....B-3
AUBURN.....D-4
BAY MINETTE.....B-7
BESSEMER.....B-3
BIRMINGHAM.....B-3
BOAZ.....C-2
BRANTLEY.....C-5
BREWTON.....B-6
BRIDGEPORT.....D-1
CARBON HILL.....B-3
CENTRE.....D-2
CENTREVILLE.....B-4
CULLMAN.....C-2
DADEVILLE.....D-4
DAUPHIN ISLAND.....A-7
DECATUR.....B-1
DEMOPOLIS.....B-4
DOTHAN.....D-6
DOUBLE SPRINGS.....B-2
ELBA.....C-6
ENTERPRISE.....C-6
EUFAULA.....D-5
EUTAW.....A-4
EVERGREEN.....B-6
FAIRFIELD.....B-3
FAIRHOPE.....A-7
FAYETTE.....A-3
FLORALA.....C-6
FLORENCE.....A-1
FORT PAYNE.....D-2
GADSDEN.....D-2
GRAND BAY.....A-7
GREENVILLE.....B-5
GROVE HILL.....B-5
GUIN.....A-2
GUNTERSVILLE.....C-2
HAMILTON.....A-2
HARTSELLE.....B-1
HEFLIN.....D-3
HUNTSVILLE.....C-1
JACKSON.....A-6
JASPER.....B-2
MULLEN.....B-1
LAFAYETTE.....D-4
LINETT.....D-4
LINDEN.....B-4
LUVERNE.....C-5
MADRID.....D-6
MCINTOSH.....A-6
MERIDIANVILLE.....C-1
MIDWAY.....D-5
MOBILE.....A-7
MONTGOMERY.....C-5
MOULTON.....B-2
MOUNT VERNON.....A-6
OPELIKA.....D-4

OPP.....C-6
OXFORD.....D-3
OZARK.....D-6
PHENIX CITY.....D-4
PIEDMONT.....D-2
PRATTVILLE.....C-4
PRICHARD.....A-7
REFORM.....A-3
ROANOKE.....D-3
RUSSELLVILLE.....A-1
SCOTTSBORO.....D-1
SELMA.....B-4
SHEFFIELD.....B-1
SILAS.....A-5
SYLACAUGA.....C-3
TALLADEGA.....C-3
TROY.....C-5
TUSCALOOSA.....A-3
TUSCUMBIA.....A-1
UNION SPRINGS.....D-5
UNIONTOWN.....B-4
WINFIELD.....A-2

ALASKA
AKUTAN.....A-5
ALAKANUK.....A-3
ANCHORAGE.....C-4
ANVIK.....B-3
BARROW.....C-1
BETHEL.....B-3
CANTWELL.....D-3
CHIGNIK.....B-5
COLD BAY.....A-5
COLLEGE.....C-3
CORDOVA.....D-4
DELTA JCT......D-3
DUTCH HARBOR.....A-5
FAIRBANKS.....D-3
FORT YUKON.....D-2
GLENNALLEN.....D-3
GOODNEWS BAY.....A-4
HAINES.....E-4
HOMER.....C-3
HOUSTON.....C-3
JUNEAU.....E-4
KALTAG.....C-3
KENAI.....C-3
KETCHIKAN.....F-5
KODIAK.....C-4
KOYUK.....B-2
NAKNEK.....B-4
NOME.....B-2
OPHIR.....C-3
PALMER.....D-4
PELICAN.....E-4
POINT HOPE.....B-1
PRUDHOE BAY.....D-1
RUBY.....C-3
SAND POINT.....B-5
SAVOONGA.....A-2
SCAMMON BAY.....A-3
SELAWIK.....B-2
SELDOVIA.....C-4
SEWARD.....D-4
SITKA.....E-5

SKAGWAY.....E-4
SLANA.....D-3
TALKEETNA.....D-3
TOK.....D-3
TUNUNAK.....A-3
UNALAKLEET.....B-3
VALDEZ.....D-3
WALES.....B-2
WHITTIER.....D-4
WRANGELL.....F-5
YAKUTAT.....E-4

ARIZONA
AGUILA.....B-5
ALPINE.....E-5
AMADO.....C-7
APACHE.....E-7
ASH FORK.....B-4
BENSON.....D-6
BISBEE.....D-7
BITTER SPRINGS.....C-2
BLACK CANYON CITY.....C-4
BUCKEYE.....B-5
BYLAS.....D-5
CAMERON.....B-3
CAMP VERDE.....C-4
CHANDLER.....B-5
CHINLE.....D-3
CHINO VALLEY.....B-4
CONGRESS.....B-4
DOUGLAS.....E-7
DUNCAN.....E-6
EHRENBERG.....A-5
ELOY.....C-6
FLAGSTAFF.....C-4
FLORENCE.....C-5
FREDONIA.....B-2
GANADO.....E-3
GILA BEND.....B-5
GLENDALE.....B-5
GLOBE.....D-5
GRAND CANYON.....B-3
GUTHRIE.....E-5
HEBER.....D-4
HOLBROOK.....D-4
JACOB LAKE.....B-2
KAYENTA.....D-2
KINGMAN.....A-3
KIRKLAND JCTN.....B-4
MARBLE CANYON.....C-2
MESA.....C-5
MEXICAN WATER.....D-2
MIAMI.....C-5
MOHAWK.....A-6
MORENCI.....D-5
NOGALES.....D-7
ORO VALLEY.....C-6
PAGE.....C-2
PAYSON.....C-4
PHOENIX.....C-5
PICACHO.....C-6
PRESCOTT.....B-4
QUARTZSITE.....A-5
RYE.....C-4

SAFFORD.....D-6
SAN LUIS.....A-6
SAN SIMON.....E-6
SANDERS.....E-4
SELIGMAN.....B-3
SHOW LOW.....D-4
SNOWFLAKE.....D-4
ST. JOHNS.....D-4
SUN CITY.....B-5
SUPERIOR.....C-5
TACNA.....A-6
TEEC NOS POS.....E-2
TEMPE.....C-5
TOMBSTONE.....D-7
TONALEA.....D-3
TONOPAH.....B-5
TOPOCK.....A-4
TUBA CITY.....C-3
TUCSON.....C-6
TUMACACORI.....C-7
VAIL.....D-6
WENDEN.....B-5
WICKENBURG.....B-5
WIKIEUP.....B-4
WILLCOX.....D-6
WILLIAMS.....C-3
WINSLOW.....C-4
YUCCA.....A-4
YUMA.....A-6

ARKANSAS
ALMA.....A-2
ARKADELPHIA.....C-4
ASH FLAT.....D-2
BALD KNOB.....D-2
BATESVILLE.....D-2
BENTON.....C-3
BERRYVILLE.....B-1
BRINKLEY.....D-3
CAMDEN.....B-5
CLARENDON.....D-4
CLARKSVILLE.....C-2
CLINTON.....C-2
CONWAY.....C-3
CORNING.....E-1
CROSSETT.....D-6
DARDANELLE.....B-3
DE QUEEN.....A-5
DERMOTT.....D-5
DUMAS.....D-5
EL DORADO.....C-6
ENGLAND.....C-3
EUREKA SPRINGS.....B-1
FAYETTEVILLE.....A-2
FORDYCE.....C-5
FOREST CITY.....E-3
FORT SMITH.....A-3
FULTON.....B-5
GLENWOOD.....B-4
HAMBURG.....D-6
HARDY.....D-1
HARRISON.....B-2

HEBER SPRINGS.....D-3
HELENA.....E-4
HOT SPRINGS.....B-4
HUGHES.....E-3
IMBODEN.....E-2
JACKSONVILLE.....D-3
JONESBORO.....E-2
JUNCTION CITY.....B-6
LAKE VILLAGE.....D-5
LEWISVILLE.....A-6
LITTLE ROCK.....B-3
MAGNOLIA.....B-6
MALVERN.....C-4
MANSFIELD.....A-3
MARIANNA.....E-4
MARKED TREE.....E-3
MARSHALL.....C-2
MCCRORY.....D-3
MCGEHEE.....D-5
MENA.....A-4
MONTICELLO.....D-5
MONTROSE.....D-6
MORRILTON.....B-3
MOUNT IDA.....B-4
MOUNTAIN HOME.....C-1
NEWPORT.....D-2
N. LITTLE ROCK.....C-4
OLA.....B-3
PARAGOULD.....E-2
PELSOR.....C-2
PIGGOTT.....E-1
PINE BLUFF.....C-4
POCAHONTAS.....D-1
PRESCOTT.....B-5
ROGERS.....A-1
RUSSELLVILLE.....B-3
SEARCY.....D-3
SHERIDAN.....C-4
SILOAM SPRINGS.....A-1
SPRINGDALE.....A-2
STAR CITY.....D-5
STUTTGART.....D-4
TEXARKANA.....A-5
VAN BUREN.....A-3
WALDO.....B-5
WALDRON.....A-3
WALNUT RIDGE.....E-2
WEST MEMPHIS.....E-3
WYNNE.....E-3
YELLVILLE.....C-2

CALIFORNIA
ADIN.....C-1
ALTURAS.....C-1
ANAHEIM.....D-6
ARCATA.....A-1
AUBURN.....C-3
AVALON.....D-7
BAKER.....E-5
BAKERSFIELD.....D-5
BARSTOW.....E-5
BELDEN.....B-2
BENTON.....D-4
BERKELEY.....B-3
BIEBER.....B-1
BIG SUR.....B-5
BISHOP.....D-4
BLACKWELLS CORNER.....C-5
BLAIRSDEN.....C-2
BLYTHE.....F-6
BRADLEY.....C-5
BRAWLEY.....F-7
BRIDGEPORT.....C-3
BURNEY.....B-1
CALEXICO.....F-7
CAMBRIA.....B-5
CANBY.....B-1
CANTIL.....D-5
CHICO.....B-2
CHULA VISTA.....D-7
COACHELLA.....E-6
CORNING.....B-2
CRESCENT CITY.....A-1
DAVIS CREEK.....C-1
DELANO.....D-5
DESERT CENTER.....F-6
DORRIS.....B-1
DOYLE.....C-2
DUNSMUIR.....B-1
EL CAJON.....E-7
EL CENTRO.....E-7

ESCONDIDO.....E-7
EUREKA.....A-1
EXETER.....D-5
FORTUNA.....A-2
FOUR CORNERS.....D-5
FRESNO.....C-4
GAVIOTA.....C-6
GILROY.....B-4
GRASS VALLEY.....B-2
GREENFIELD.....B-5
GRIDLEY.....B-2
HANFORD.....C-5
HAYWARD.....B-4
HOLLISTER.....B-4
HUNTINGTON BCH.....D-6
INDEPENDENCE.....D-4
INGLEWOOD.....D-6
JACKSON.....C-3
KING CITY.....B-5
KLAMATH.....A-1
LAKESIDE.....E-7
LANCASTER.....D-6
LEE VINING.....D-3
LIKELY.....C-1
LODI.....B-3
LOLETA.....A-2
LOMPOC.....C-6
LONE PINE.....D-4
LONG BEACH.....D-6
LOS ANGELES.....D-6
LOS BANOS.....C-4
LOS MOLINOS.....B-2
LOS OLIVOS.....C-6
LUCIA.....B-5
LUDLOW.....E-6
MADERA.....C-4
MANTECA.....B-4
MARIPOSA.....C-4
MARYSVILLE.....B-3
MCKINLEYVILLE.....A-1
MERCED.....C-4
MODESTO.....C-4
MOJAVE.....D-5
MONTEREY.....B-4
MORRO BAY.....B-5
NAPA.....B-3
NEEDLES.....F-5
NICE.....B-3
OAKLAND.....B-4
OCEANSIDE.....D-7
OLANCHA.....D-5
ONTARIO.....D-6
ORICK.....A-1
ORLAND.....B-2
OROVILLE.....B-2
OXNARD.....D-6
PACIFICA.....A-4
PALM SPRINGS.....E-6
PASADENA.....D-6
PETALUMA.....A-3
PISMO BEACH.....B-5
PLACERVILLE.....C-3
POMONA.....D-6
QUINCY.....B-2
RED BLUFF.....B-2
REDDING.....B-2
REDWAY.....A-2
RICHMOND.....A-3
RIDGECREST.....D-5
RIVERSIDE.....E-6
ROSEVILLE.....B-3
SACRAMENTO.....B-3
SALINAS.....B-4
SAN BERNARDINO.....E-6
SAN DIEGO.....D-7
SAN FRANCISCO.....A-4
SAN JOSE.....B-4
SAN LUIS OBISPO.....C-5
SAN MATEO.....A-4
SAN RAFAEL.....A-3
SAN SIMEON.....B-5
SANGER.....C-4
SANTA ANA.....D-6
SANTA BARBARA.....C-6
SANTA CRUZ.....B-4
SANTA MARIA.....C-6
SANTA ROSA.....A-3
SELMA.....C-4
SHASTA LAKE.....B-2
SMITH RIVER.....A-1
SONORA.....C-3
STOCKTON.....B-3
SUNNYVALE.....B-4
SUSANVILLE.....C-2
TEHACHAPI.....D-5

TEMECULA.....E-6
TERMO.....C-1
THOUSAND OAKS.....C-6
TRACY.....B-4
TULARE.....C-5
TURLOCK.....C-4
UKIAH.....A-3
VALLEJO.....B-3
VENTURA.....C-6
VICTORVILLE.....E-6
VISALIA.....C-4
WASCO.....C-5
WATSONVILLE.....B-4
WEAVERVILLE.....A-1
WEED.....B-1
WILLIAMS.....B-3
WILLITS.....A-2
WILLOWS.....B-3
WOODLAND.....B-3
YREKA.....B-1
YUBA CITY.....B-3
YUCCA VALLEY.....E-6

COLORADO
AKRON.....F-1
ALAMOSA.....D-4
ANTON.....F-2
ANTONITO.....D-5
ARVADA.....D-2
AULT.....E-1
AURORA.....D-2
BLANCA.....D-5
BOULDER.....D-2
BRIGHTON.....D-2
BURLINGTON.....F-2
CAMPO.....G-5
CANON CITY.....D-3
CHEYENNE WELLS.....F-3
CLIFTON.....B-3
COLORADO SPRNGS.....E-3
COPE.....F-2
CORTEZ.....A-4
CRAIG.....B-1
DE BEQUE.....B-2
DEL NORTE.....C-4
DELTA.....B-3
DENVER.....D-2
DINOSAUR.....A-1
DOVE CREEK.....A-4
DURANGO.....B-4
EADS.....F-3
EMPIRE.....C-2
EVANS.....E-1
FAIRPLAY.....D-3
FORT COLLINS.....D-1
FORT LUPTON.....E-2
FORT MORGAN.....E-2
FOWLER.....E-4
FRISCO.....D-2
FRUITA.....A-3
GLENWOOD SPRGS.....C-2
GRANBY.....D-2
GRAND JUNCTION.....A-3
GREELEY.....E-1
GUNNISON.....C-3
GYPSUM.....C-2
HAXTUN.....F-1
HAYDEN.....C-1
HOLLY.....G-4
HOLYOKE.....F-1
HUGO.....F-2
IDALIA.....G-2
KIT CARSON.....F-3
KREMMLING.....C-2
LA JARA.....D-5
LAJUNTA.....F-4
LAKEWOOD.....D-2
LAMAR.....G-4
LAST CHANCE.....F-2
LEADVILLE.....C-2
LIMON.....E-2
LITTLETON.....E-2
LONGMONT.....D-1
LOVELAND.....D-1
MANCOS.....B-4
MEEKER.....B-2
MINTURN.....C-2
MONTE VISTA.....D-4
MONTROSE.....B-3
NEW CASTLE.....B-2
OLATHE.....B-3
OURAY.....B-3
PAGOSA SPRINGS.....C-5
PUEBLO.....E-3
RAMAH.....E-3

RIDGWAY.....B-4
RIFLE.....B-2
SAGUACHE.....C-4
SALIDA.....D-3
SILVERTON.....B-4
SIMLA.....E-3
SPRINGFIELD.....F-4
STEAMBOAT SPRS.....C-1
STERLING.....F-1
THORNTON.....E-2
TRINIDAD.....E-5
WALSENBURG.....E-4
WIGGINS.....E-2
WINTER PARK.....D-2
YUMA.....F-2

CONNECTICUT
ANDOVER.....D-2
ANSONIA.....B-3
ASHFORD.....E-2
AVON.....C-2
BRIDGEPORT.....B-4
BRISTOL.....B-2
BROOKFIELD.....B-3
CANAAN.....B-1
CHESTER.....D-3
COLCHESTER.....D-3
DANBURY.....A-3
ENFIELD.....C-1
FAIRFIELD.....B-4
GRANBY.....C-1
GREENWICH.....A-5
GROTON.....E-4
HAMDEN.....C-3
HAMPTON.....E-2
HARTFORD.....D-2
HEBRON.....D-3
KENT.....A-2
LITCHFIELD.....B-2
MANCHESTER.....D-2
MARLBOROUGH.....D-3
MERIDEN.....C-3
MIDDLETOWN.....C-3
MILFORD.....B-4
MYSTIC.....E-4
NAUGATUCK.....C-3
NEWBRITAIN.....C-3
NEW HARTFORD.....B-2
NEWHAVEN.....C-4
NEW LONDON.....E-4
NEW MILFORD.....B-3
NORFOLK.....B-1
NORWALK.....B-4
NORWICH.....E-3
PUTNAM.....E-2
SHELTON.....B-4
SIMSBURY.....C-2
STAMFORD.....A-5
THOMASTON.....B-2
THOMPSON.....E-1
TORRINGTON.....B-2
TRUMBULL.....B-4
UNION.....E-1
WALLINGFORD.....C-3
WATERBURY.....C-3
WEST HAVEN.....C-4
WILTON.....A-4
WINSTED.....B-2

DELAWARE
BETHANY BEACH.....D-6
BOWERS BEACH.....C-4
BRIDGEVILLE.....B-5
DOVER.....C-4
GEORGETOWN.....C-6
LAUREL.....B-6
LEWES.....D-5
MIDDLETOWN.....B-3
MILFORD.....C-5
MILLSBORO.....C-6
NEW CASTLE.....B-2
NEWARK.....A-2
SEAFORD.....B-6
SMYRNA.....C-3
WILMINGTON.....B-1

FLORIDA
ALVA.....F-5
APALACHICOLA.....C-2
ARCADIA.....F-5
ASTOR.....F-3
AVON PARK.....F-4
BALDWIN.....E-2
BAYONET POINT.....E-3
BELLE GLADE.....G-5

Places Index

BONITA SPRINGS F-5
BRADENTON.....E-4
BROOKSVILLE.....E-3
BUNNELL.....F-2
CAPE CANAVERAL..G-3
CAPE CORAL.....E-5
CARRABELLE.....C-2
CEDAR KEY.....D-3
CHIEFLAND.....E-2
CLEARWATER.....E-4
CLERMONT.....F-3
CLEWISTON.....G-5
COCOA.....G-3
CORAL GABLES G-6
CORAL SPRINGS G-5
CRAWFORDVILLE.....C-2
CRESCENT BEACH F-2
CRESTVIEW.....B-1
CRYSTAL RIVER E-3
DAYTONA BEACH G-3
DE LAND F-3
DEFUNIAK SPRINGS..B-1
DELTONA.....F-3
DUNEDIN.....E-4
EASTPOINT.....C-2
EDGEWATER.....G-3
ENGLEWOOD.....E-5
FERNANDINA BEACH F-1
FLAGLER BEACH F-2
FORT LAUDERDALE ..G-6
FORT MYERS.....F-5
FORT PIERCE.....G-4
FORT WALTON BCH...B-1
GAINESVILLE.....F-2
GOLDEN GATE F-6
GREEN COVE SPGS....F-2
HAINES CITY F-3
HAWTHORNE.....F-2
HIGH SPRINGS.....E-2
HOLLYWOOD.....G-6
HOMESTEAD.....G-6
HOMOSASSA SPRGS ..D-3
JACKSONVILLE.....F-1
JACKSONVILLE BCH ..F-1
JUPITER.....G-5
KEY LARGO......G-7
KEY WEST.....F-7
KISSIMMEE.....F-4
LAKE BUTLER.....E-2
LAKE CITY.....E-2
LAKE WORTH.....G-5
LAKELAND.....E-4
LARGO.....E-4
LEESBURG.....F-3
LIVE OAK.....E-2
LUTZ.....E-4
LYNN HAVEN.....B-1
MARATHON.....F-7
MARCO.....F-6
MARIANNA.....C-1
MAYO.....D-2
MELBOURNE.....G-4
MERRITT ISLAND..G-3
MIAMI.....G-6
MILTON.....A-1
MIMS.....G-3
MONTICELLO.....D-1
NAPLES.....F-6
NEW PORT RICHEY...D-4
NEW SMYRNA BCH...G-3
OCALA.....F-3
OKEECHOBEE F-5
ORLANDO.....F-4
ORMOND BEACH G-2
PALATKA.....F-2
PALM BAY.....G-4
PALM COAST.....F-2
PANAMA CITY.....B-2
PENSACOLA.....A-1
PERRINE.....G-6
PERRY.....D-2
PORT CHARLOTTE F-5
PORT ORANGE G-3
PORT ST. LUCIE.....G-4
PORT ST. JOE.....B-2
PUNTA GORDA F-5
QUINCY.....C-1
SANFORD.....F-3
SANIBEL.....E-5
SARASOTA.....E-4
SEBASTIAN.....G-4
SEBRING.....F-4
SPRING HILL.....E-3
SPRINGFIELD B-2
ST. AUGUSTINE.....F-2
ST. CLOUD.....F-4

ST. PETERSBURG D-4
STARKE.....E-2
STUART.....G-5
TALLAHASSEE.....C-2
TAMPA.....E-4
TITUSVILLE.....G-3
VENICE.....E-5
VERO BEACH.....G-4
WALDO.....E-2
WEST PALM BEACH..G-5
WILDWOOD.....F-3
WINTER HAVEN F-4
YULEE.....F-1

GEORGIA
ABBEVILLE.....C-4
ALAPAHA.....C-5
ALBANY.....B-5
ALMA.....C-5
AMERICUS.....B-4
ATHENS.....C-2
ATLANTA.....B-2
AUGUSTA.....D-3
BAINBRIDGE.....B-5
BAXLEY.....D-4
BLAIRSVILLE.....B-1
BLUE RIDGE.....B-1
BREMEN.....A-2
BRUNSWICK..G-5
CAIRO.....B-6
CAMILLA.....B-5
CARROLLTON.....A-3
CARTERSVILLE.....A-2
CEDARTOWN.....A-2
CHATSWORTH A-1
CLARKESVILLE B-1
CLAXTON.....D-4
COLQUITT A-5
COLUMBUS.....A-4
CORDELE.....C-4
CORNELIA.....B-2
COVINGTON.....B-3
CUTHBERT A-4
DARIEN.....D-5
DAWSON.....B-4
DAWSONVILLE.....B-2
DONALSONVILLE.....A-5
DOUGLAS.....C-5
DUBLIN.....C-4
EAST POINT.....A-2
EASTMAN.....C-4
EATONTON.....C-3
ELLAVILLE.....B-4
FOLKSTON.....D-6
GAINESVILLE B-2
GEORGETOWN.....A-4
GLENVILLE.....D-4
GRIFFIN.....B-3
HAZLEHURST.....C-4
HOMERVILLE.....C-5
JESUP.....D-5
KINGSLAND D-6
LA FAYETTE.....A-1
LA GRANGE.....A-3
LOUISVILLE.....C-3
LUDOWICI.....D-5
LYONS.....D-4
MACON.....B-3
MADISON.....C-3
MARIETTA.....A-2
MCRAE.....C-4
MILLEDGEVILLE.....C-3
MOULTRIE.....B-5
NAHUNTA.....D-5
PATTERSON D-5
PEARSON.....C-5
PERRY.....B-4
QUITMAN.....B-6
RICHLAND.....A-4
ROBERTA.....B-4
ROME.....A-2
ROSWELL.....B-2
SAVANNAH.....D-4
SPARTA.....C-3
STATESBORO.....D-4
SUMMERVILLE.....A-2
SWAINSBORO.....D-4
SYLVESTER.....B-5
TALBOTTON.....A-3
THOMASTON.....A-3
THOMASVILLE.....B-6
THOMSON.....C-3
TIFTON.....C-5
VALDOSTA C-6
VIDALIA.....D-4
WARNER ROBINS.....B-4

WASHINGTON C-2
WAYCROSS.....D-5
WAYNESBORO D-3
WINDER B-2
WRENS.....C-3

HAWAII
CAPTAIN COOK.....E-4
HAENA.....A-1
HALAWA.....A-1
HANA.....F-3
HILO.....G-4
HONOKAA.....F-3
HONOKOHAU E-2
HONOLULU.....C-2
KAILUA.....B-1
KAILUA-KONA.....E-4
KAPAA.....B-1
KAPOHO.....G-4
KAUNAKAKAI..D-2
KAWAIHAE.....E-3
KEAAU.....G-4
KEKAHA.....A-1
KEOKEA.....F-4
KIHEI.....E-3
KILAUEA.....B-1
LAHAINA.....E-2
LAIE.....C-1
LANAI CITY.....D-2
LAUPAHOEHOE.....G-3
LIHUE.....B-1
MAUNALOA.....D-2
NAALEHU.....F-5
NANAKULI.....C-2
PAHALA.....F-4
PAPA.....F-4
ULUPALAKUA.....E-3
VOLCANO.....G-4
WAIANAE.....C-2
WAIMEA.....F-3

IDAHO
AMERICAN FALLS......C-6
ARCO.....C-6
ASHTON.....E-5
ATOMIC CITY.....C-6
BANKS.....A-5
BELLEVUE.....C-6
BLACKFOOT.....D-6
BLISS.....B-6
BOISE.....A-6
BONNERS FERRY.....A-1
BURLEY.....C-7
CALDWELL.....A-6
CAMBRIDGE.....A-5
CAREY.....C-6
CARMEN.....C-4
CASCADE.....A-5
CHALLIS.....B-5
COEUR D'ALENE.....A-2
COTTONWOOD.....A-3
COUNCIL.....A-5
DONNELLY.....A-5
DOWNEY.....D-7
DUBOIS.....D-5
EASTPORT.....A-1
ELLIS.....C-5
FAIRFIELD.....B-6
FENN.....A-4
FRANKLIN.....D-7
GARDEN CITY A-6
GEORGETOWN E-7
GLENNS FERRY B-6
GOODING.....B-6
GRANGEVILLE.....A-4
GREER.....A-3
HAILEY.....C-6
HILL CITY.....B-6
HOLLISTER.....B-7
IDAHO FALLS.....D-6
ISLAND PARK.....E-5
JEROME.....B-7
KAMIAH.....B-3
KELLOGG.....A-2
KETCHUM.....B-6
KOOSKIA.....B-3
LAKEVIEW.....A-2
LEWISTON.....A-3
LOWELL.....B-3
LUCILE.....A-4
MACKAY.....C-5
MALAD CITY.....D-7
MCCALL.....A-5
MCCAMMON.....D-7
MIDVALE.....A-5

MONTPELIER E-7
MOORE.....C-6
MOSCOW.....A-3
MOUNTAIN HOME..A-6
MOYIE SPRINGS A-1
NAMPA.....A-6
NEW MEADOWS A-4
PARIS.....D-7
PARMA.....A-5
PAYETTE.....A-5
PLUMMER.....A-2
POCATELLO.....D-6
POTLATCH.....A-3
PRESTON.....D-7
PRIEST RIVER A-2
REXBURG.....D-5
RICHFIELD.....C-6
RIGBY.....D-6
RIGGINS.....A-4
ROGERSON.....B-7
RUPERT.....C-7
SALMON.....C-4
SANDPOINT.....A-1
SHOSHONE.....C-6
SMITHS FERRY.....A-5
SODA SPRINGS.....D-6
SPENCER.....D-5
ST. ANTHONY.....D-5
STANLEY.....B-5
SUNBEAM.....B-5
TWIN FALLS.....B-7
WALLACE.....A-2
WEISER.....A-5
WHITE BIRD.....A-4
WINCHESTER.....A-3

ILLINOIS
ALTON.....B-5
ARCOLA.....D-4
AURORA.....D-2
BARTONVILLE.....B-3
BEARDSTOWN.....B-4
BELLEVILLE.....B-6
BELVIDERE.....C-1
BLOOMINGTON.....C-3
CAIRO.....C-7
CAMP POINT.....A-4
CARBONDALE.....C-7
CARMI.....D-6
CENTRALIA.....C-6
CHAMPAIGN.....D-4
CHENOA.....C-3
CHESTER.....B-6
CHICAGO.....D-1
CHRISMAN.....D-4
CLINTON.....C-4
COLLINSVILLE.....B-5
DANVILLE.....D-4
DE KALB.....C-1
DECATUR.....C-4
DIXON.....B-2
DU QUOIN.....C-6
EFFINGHAM.....C-5
ELGIN.....D-1
EUREKA.....C-3
EVANSTON.....D-1
FLORA.....D-5
GALENA.....D-1
GALESBURG.....B-3
HAMILTON.....A-3
HARRISBURG.....D-7
HAVANA.....B-3
HEYWORTH.....C-3
JACKSONVILLE.....B-4
JOLIET.....D-2
KANKAKEE.....C-2
KEWANEE.....B-2
LA SALLE.....B-2
LAWRENCEVILLE.....D-5
LEWISTOWN.....B-3
LEXINGTON.....C-3
LINCOLN.....C-4
MENDOTA.....C-2
MILFORD.....D-3
MOLINE.....B-2
MONMOUTH.....B-2
MONTICELLO.....D-4
MORRIS.....C-2
MORTON.....D-3
MOUNT CARMEL.....D-6
MOUNT CARROLL.....B-1
MOUNT VERNON.....C-6

MURPHYSBORO C-6
NASHVILLE.....C-6
NORMAL.....C-3
OLNEY.....C-6
OREGON.....C-1
PANA.....C-5
PARIS.....D-4
PAXTON.....D-3
PEKIN.....B-3
PEORIA.....B-3
PEORIA HEIGHTS B-3
PRINCETON.....B-2
QUINCY.....A-4
RANTOUL.....D-3
RED BUD.....B-6
ROCK FALLS.....C-2
ROCK ISLAND.....A-2
ROCKFORD.....C-1
ROSSVILLE.....D-3
RUSHVILLE.....B-4
SALEM.....C-6
SHAWNEETOWN D-6
SPRINGFIELD.....C-4
STERLING.....B-2
STOCKTON.....B-1
SYCAMORE.....C-1
URBANA.....D-4
VANDALIA.....C-5
VIENNA.....C-7
WATERLOO.....B-6
WATSEKA.....D-3
WAUKEGAN.....D-1

INDIANA
ALEXANDRIA.....C-3
ANDERSON C-3
ANGOLA.....D-1
ATTICA.....B-3
AUBURN.....D-1
AURORA.....D-5
BEDFORD.....C-5
BICKNELL.....B-6
BLOOMINGTON C-5
BROWNSBURG B-4
BROWNSTOWN C-5
CHURUBUSCO.....D-2
COLUMBIA CITY D-2
COLUMBUS.....C-5
CRAWFORDSVILLE.....B-4
DALE.....B-7
DECATUR.....D-2
DELPHI.....C-3
ELKHART.....C-1
EVANSVILLE.....A-7
FORT WAYNE.....D-2
FRANKFORT.....C-3
FRANKLIN.....C-5
GARY.....B-1
GOSHEN.....C-1
GREENCASTLE.....B-4
GREENFIELD.....C-4
GREENSBURG D-5
HUNTINGBURG B-6
HUNTINGTON.....C-2
INDIANAPOLIS.....B-4
JASPER.....B-6
JEFFERSONVILLE..D-6
KENDALLVILLE.....D-1
KENTLAND.....B-3
KNIGHTSTOWN D-4
KNOX.....B-1
KOKOMO.....C-3
LA PORTE.....B-1
LAFAYETTE B-3
LAGRANGE.....D-1
LEBANON.....B-4
LIBERTY.....D-4
LOGANSPORT B-2
LOOGOOTEE.....B-6
LYNN.....D-3
MADISON.....D-6
MARION.....C-3
MEDARYVILLE.....B-2
MICHIGAN CITY B-1
MISHAWAKA.....C-1
MONTICELLO.....B-2
MOORESVILLE.....B-4
MOUNT VERNON.....A-7
MUNCIE.....D-3
NASHVILLE.....C-5
NEW ALBANY.....C-6

NEW CASTLE.....D-4
NOBLESVILLE.....C-3
NORTH VERNON.....D-5
PALMYRA.....C-6
PAOLI.....C-6
PERU.....C-2
PLYMOUTH.....C-2
PORTLAND.....D-3
PRINCETON.....A-6
RENSSELAER.....B-2
RICHMOND.....D-4
ROCKVILLE.....B-4
RUSHVILLE.....D-4
SEYMOUR.....C-5
SOUTH BEND.....B-1
SPENCER.....B-5
SULLIVAN.....B-5
TERRE HAUTE.....B-4
VALPARAISO.....B-1
VEEDERSBURG.....B-3
VERSAILLES.....D-5
WABASH.....C-2
WALKERTON.....C-1
WARSAW.....C-2
WASHINGTON.....B-6
WINAMAC.....B-2
WINCHESTER.....D-3
WORTHINGTON.....B-5

IOWA
ALGONA.....C-1
AMES.....D-3
ATLANTIC.....C-3
BLOOMFIELD.....E-4
BURLINGTON.....F-4
CARROLL.....C-2
CASCADE.....F-2
CEDAR FALLS.....E-2
CEDAR RAPIDS.....F-3
CHARITON.....D-4
CHARLES CITY.....E-1
CHEROKEE.....B-2
CLARINDA.....B-4
CLINTON.....G-3
CORNING.....C-4
COUNCIL BLUFFS.....B-4
CRESTON.....C-4
DAVENPORT.....F-3
DECORAH.....F-1
DENISON.....B-3
DES MOINES.....D-3
DUBUQUE.....F-2
DYERSVILLE.....F-2
FAIRFIELD.....E-4
FORT DODGE.....C-2
FORT MADISON.....F-4
GARNER.....D-1
GLENWOOD.....B-4
GREENSBURG.....C-4? — **GUTTENBERG**.....F-2
HARLAN.....B-3
HOLSTEIN.....B-2
HUMBOLDT.....C-2
INDEPENDENCE.....E-2
INDIANOLA.....D-3
IOWA CITY.....F-3
IOWA FALLS.....D-2
KEOKUK.....F-4
LE MARS.....B-2
MAQUOKETA.....F-2
MASON CITY.....D-1
MISSOURI VALLEY.....B-3
MONTEZUMA.....E-3
MONTICELLO.....F-2
MOUNT AYR.....C-4
MOUNT PLEASANT ..E-4
MUSCATINE.....F-3
NASHUA.....E-1
NEW HAMPTON.....E-1
NEW LONDON.....F-4
NEW SHARON.....E-3
NEWTON.....D-3
OAKLAND.....B-3
OGDEN.....C-2
OSAGE.....E-1
OSCEOLA.....D-4
OSKALOOSA.....D-3
OTTUMWA.....E-4
PARKERSBURG.....E-2
PERRY.....C-3
POSTVILLE.....F-1
RED OAK.....B-4
ROCK RAPIDS.....B-1
ROCKWELL CITY.....C-2
SAC CITY.....C-2
SHELDON.....B-1

SHENANDOAH B-4
SIBLEY.....B-1
SIDNEY.....B-4
SIOUX CITY.....A-2
SPENCER.....B-1
SPIRIT LAKE.....B-1
STORM LAKE.....B-2
TAMA.....E-3
TRAER.....E-2
VINTON.....E-2
WAPELLO.....F-4
WATERLOO.....E-2
WAVERLY.....E-2
WEST UNION.....F-1
WILLIAMSBURG.....E-3
WINTERSET.....C-3
WOODBINE.....B-3

KANSAS
ABILENE.....E-2
ARKANSAS CITY.....E-4
ARMA.....G-4
ATWOOD.....B-1
AUGUSTA.....E-4
BAXTER SPRINGS.....G-4
BELLEVILLE.....E-1
BLUE RAPIDS.....E-1
BUCKLIN.....C-4
BURLINGTON.....F-3
CALDWELL.....D-4
CANEY.....G-4
CHANUTE.....G-4
CHERRYVALE.....G-4
CIMARRON.....B-3
COFFEYVILLE.....G-4
CONCORDIA.....D-1
DERBY.....E-4
DODGE CITY.....B-3
DOUGLASS.....E-4
EL DORADO.....E-3
ELKHART.....A-4
ELLINWOOD.....D-3
ELLIS.....C-2
ELLSWORTH.....D-3
EMPORIA.....F-3
EUREKA.....F-3
FLORENCE.....E-3
FORT SCOTT.....G-3
GARNETT.....G-3
GOODLAND.....A-2
GREAT BEND.....C-3
GREENSBURG.....C-4
HAYS.....C-2
HAYSVILLE.....E-4
HERINGTON.....E-2
HILL CITY.....C-2
HOISINGTON.....D-3
HOLTON.....F-1
HUTCHINSON.....D-3
INDEPENDENCE.....G-3
IOLA.....G-3
JETMORE.....B-3
JUNCTION CITY.....E-2
KANSAS CITY.....G-2
KINGMAN.....D-4
KINSLEY.....C-3
LAKIN.....A-3
LARNED.....C-3
LAWRENCE.....F-2
LIBERAL.....B-4
LOUISBURG.....G-2
LYONS.....D-3
MANKATO.....D-1
MARYSVILLE.....F-1
MCPHERSON.....D-3
MEADE.....B-4
MEDICINE LODGE.....D-4
MINNEOLA.....C-4
MORAN.....G-3
NEODESHA.....F-4
NESS CITY.....B-3
NEWTON.....E-3
NORTON.....C-1
OAKLEY.....B-1
OBERLIN.....B-1
OLATHE.....G-2
OSAWATOMIE.....G-3
OSBORNE.....D-2
OTTAWA.....F-2
PEABODY.....E-3
PHILLIPSBURG.....C-1
PITTSBURG.....G-4
PLEASANTON.....G-3
PRATT.....D-4
QUINTER.....B-2

RILEY.....E-2
RUSSELL.....C-2
SABETHA.....F-1
SALINA.....D-2
SCOTT CITY.....B-3
SENECA.....F-1
SHARON SPRINGS.....A-2
SMITH CENTER.....D-1
ST. FRANCIS.....A-1
ST. JOHN.....D-3
STAFFORD.....D-3
SYRACUSE.....A-3
TOPEKA.....F-2
TROY.....G-1
VICTORIA.....C-2
WAKEENEY.....C-2
WASHINGTON.....E-1
WICHITA.....E-4
WILSON.....D-2
WINFIELD.....E-4
YATES CENTER.....F-3

KENTUCKY
ALBANY.....E-4
ASHLAND.....G-2
BARDSTOWN.....D-3
BARDWELL.....A-4
BEDFORD.....D-2
BOWLING GREEN C-4
BUTLER.....E-1
CAMPTON.....F-3
CENTRAL CITY.....C-3
CORBIN.....F-3
COVINGTON.....E-1
CUMBERLAND.....G-3
CYNTHIANA.....E-2
ELIZABETHTOWN.....D-3
FRANKFORT.....D-2
FULTON.....A-4
GEORGETOWN.....E-2
GLASGOW.....D-4
GRAYSON.....G-2
GREENUP.....G-1
HARLAN.....G-4
HARRODSBURG.....E-3
HAZARD.....G-3
HENDERSON.....B-2
HODGENVILLE.....D-3
HOPKINSVILLE.....C-4
INEZ.....G-2
IRVINGTON.....D-3
JACKSON.....F-3
JAMESTOWN.....E-4
JENKINS.....G-3
LEITCHFIELD.....C-3
LEXINGTON.....E-2
LIVERMORE.....C-3
LONDON.....F-3
LOUISA.....G-2
LOUISVILLE.....D-2
MANCHESTER.....F-3
MARION.....B-3
MAYFIELD.....A-4
MAYSVILLE.....F-1
MIDDLESBORO.....F-4
MOREHEAD.....F-2
MORGANFIELD.....B-2
MT. VERNON.....E-3
MURRAY.....B-4
NEW CASTLE.....E-2
OWENSBORO.....C-2
OWENTON.....E-2
PADUCAH.....B-3
PARIS.....E-2
PIKEVILLE.....G-3
PRESTONSBURG.....G-2
PRINCETON.....B-3
RICHMOND.....E-3
RUSSELLVILLE.....C-4
SCOTTSVILLE.....D-4
SEBREE.....C-2
SOMERSET.....E-3
STANFORD.....E-3
VERSAILLES.....E-2
WHITESBURG.....G-3
WICKLIFFE.....A-4
WILLIAMSBURG.....F-4
WINCHESTER.....E-2

LOUISIANA
ALEXANDRIA.....C-
BASTROP.....
BATON ROUGE.....E-
BERNICE.....C-
BOSSIER CITY.....

AMPTI ...C-2
LAYTON ...D-2
OLFAX ...C-2
OUSHATTA ...F-3
ROWLEY ...C-4
E QUINCY ...B-3
E RIDDER ...A-6
ELHI ...D-1
UNICE ...C-3
ERRIDAY ...D-2
RANKLIN ...D-4
LENMORA ...C-1
RAMBLING ...C-1
AMMOND ...E-3
OMER ...E-4
OUMA ...D-2
EANERETTE ...D-2
ENA ...D-2
ENNINGS ...C-3
ONESBORO ...C-1
ONESVILLE ...D-2
ENNER ...E-3
ENTWOOD ...E-3
INDER ...C-2
AFAYETTE ...D-4
AKE CHARLES ...C-4
AKE PROVIDENCE ...D-1
ECOMPTE ...C-3
EESVILLE ...C-3
OGANSPORT ...B-2
MANSFIELD ...D-4
ANY ...D-4
ETAIRIE ...E-4
PERRYVILLE ...B-3
INDEN ...D-1
ONROE ...D-1
ONTGOMERY ...C-2
ORGAN CITY ...E-4
EW IBERIA ...D-4
EW ORLEANS ...F-4
AKDALE ...C-3
BERLIN ...C-3
PELOUSAS ...D-3
NEVILLE ...D-4
LAQUEMINE ...D-4
ORT ALLEN ...D-4
ORT SULPHUR ...F-4
AYNE ...C-4
USTON ...D-1
HREVEPORT ...B-1
LIDELL ...F-4
T. FRANCISVILLE ...D-1
ALLULAH ...D-1
HIBODAUX ...D-2
ULLOS ...D-2
ENICE ...F-5
DALIA ...B-4
NTON ...B-4
ELSH ...C-2
INNFIELD ...C-2
INNSBORO ...D-2
WOLLE ...B-2

MAINE
LFRED ...A-7
MHERST ...D-5
UBURN ...A-6
UGUSTA ...B-5
ANGOR ...D-5
AR HARBOR ...D-5
ATH ...B-6
ELFAST ...C-5
ETHEL ...A-5
INGHAM ...B-4
RUNSWICK ...C-5
UCKSPORT ...C-5
AMDEN ...C-5
ARIBOU ...D-2
HERRYFIELD ...D-5
ANFORTH ...D-3
LLSWORTH ...D-5
ARMINGTON ...A-5
RYEBURG ...A-6
RAY ...A-6
UILFORD ...B-4
ARMONY ...B-4
OLLIS CENTER ...A-6
OULTON ...D-3
LE AU HAUT ...C-3
ACKMAN ...C-3
ONESBORO ...D-5
TTERY ...A-7
GRANGE ...B-4
WISTON ...B-6

LINCOLN ...C-4
MACHIAS ...D-5
MARS HILL ...D-2
MILO ...C-4
MONTICELLO ...D-2
NEWRY ...A-5
NORWAY ...A-6
PERRY ...E-4
PORTLAND ...B-6
PRESQUE ISLE ...C-2
ROCKLAND ...B-6
RUMFORD ...A-5
SANFORD ...A-7
SKOWHEGAN ...B-5
SPRINGFIELD ...D-4
STONINGTON ...C-6
THOMASTON ...B-6
TOPSFIELD ...D-4
VAN BUREN ...D-1
WATERVILLE ...B-5
WESLEY ...D-4
WEST FORKS ...B-4
WHITING ...E-5
WINTHROP ...B-5
WISCASSET ...B-6
WOODLAND ...D-4
YARMOUTH ...B-6

MARYLAND
ABERDEEN ...F-1
ACCIDENT ...A-1
ANNAPOLIS ...E-2
BALTIMORE ...E-2
BELAIR ...E-1
BERLIN ...G-4
BRANDYWINE ...E-3
CAMBRIDGE ...E-3
CLEAR SPRING ...C-1
COLUMBIA ...D-2
CRISFIELD ...F-4
CUMBERLAND ...B-1
DARLINGTON ...E-1
DENTON ...F-3
DUNDALK ...E-2
EASTON ...F-3
EDGEWOOD ...E-2
ELKTON ...F-1
EWELL ...F-4
FREDERICK ...D-1
FROSTBURG ...A-1
GERMANTOWN ...D-2
HAGERSTOWN ...C-1
HEREFORD ...E-1
INDIAN HEAD ...D-3
LAPLATA ...D-3
LEXINGTON PARK ...E-4
OCEAN CITY ...G-4
POCOMOKE CITY ...F-4
POPES CREEK ...D-3
POTOMAC ...D-2
PRINCE FREDERICK ...E-3
QUEENSTOWN ...E-2
RANDALLSTOWN ...D-2
SALISBURY ...F-4
SCOTLAND ...E-4
SEVERNA PARK ...E-2
SILVER SPRING ...D-2
SNOW HILL ...G-4
ST. CHARLES ...E-3
TIMONIUM ...E-1
UPPER MARLBORO ...E-3
VIENNA ...F-3
WASHINGTON, DC ...D-3
WESTMINSTER ...D-1

MASSACHUSETTS
AMHERST ...C-2
BALDWINVILLE ...D-1
BEDFORD ...E-2
BELCHERTOWN ...C-2
BEVERLY ...F-2
BILLERICA ...E-2
BOSTON ...E-2
BOURNE ...F-4
BROCKTON ...E-3
BROOKFIELD ...C-2
CHARLEMONT ...B-1
CHATHAM ...G-4
CHELMSFORD ...D-1
CHICOPEE ...C-3
CHILMARK ...F-5
CUMMINGTON ...B-2
DALTON ...B-2
DANVERS ...F-2
EAST FREETOWN ...F-4

EDGARTOWN ...F-4
ERVING ...C-1
FALL RIVER ...E-4
FALMOUTH ...F-4
FITCHBURG ...D-2
FRAMINGHAM ...E-2
GAY HEAD ...F-5
GLOUCESTER ...F-1
GOSHEN ...B-2
GREAT BARRINGTON ...A-2
GREENFIELD ...B-1
HAVERHILL ...E-1
HOLYOKE ...C-2
HYANNIS ...G-4
LAWRENCE ...E-1
LEE ...A-2
LEOMINSTER ...D-2
LEXINGTON ...E-2
LOWELL ...E-1
LUDLOW ...C-3
LYNN ...E-2
MADAKET ...G-5
MALDEN ...E-2
MIDDLEBORO ...F-3
MILTON ...E-2
NANTUCKET ...G-5
NEW BEDFORD ...F-4
NEWBURYPORT ...E-1
NORTH ADAMS ...B-1
NORTH TISBURY ...F-5
NORTHAMPTON ...B-2
OAK BLUFFS ...F-4
ORLEANS ...G-3
PITTSFIELD ...A-2
PLYMOUTH ...F-3
PROVINCETOWN ...G-3
QUINCY ...E-2
RANDOLPH ...E-3
SALEM ...F-2
SALISBURY ...F-1
SHEFFIELD ...A-3
SOMERVILLE ...E-2
SPENCER ...C-2
SPRINGFIELD ...C-3
STURBRIDGE ...D-3
TAUNTON ...E-3
TRURO ...G-3
WARE ...C-2
WELLFLEET ...G-3
WESTFIELD ...B-3
WESTMINISTER ...D-2
WEYMOUTH ...F-2
WINCHENDON ...C-1
WINDSOR ...B-2
WORCESTER ...D-2

MICHIGAN
ALANSON ...D-3
ALBION ...D-6
ALLEGAN ...D-6
ALMA ...E-5
ALPENA ...E-3
ANN ARBOR ...E-6
ATLANTA ...E-3
AU GRES ...E-4
BADAXE ...F-4
BALDWIN ...D-4
BARAGA ...B-1
BATTLE CREEK ...D-6
BAY CITY ...E-5
BENTON HARBOR ...C-6
BLANEY PARK ...D-2
BREVORT ...D-2
BRUCE CROSSING ...B-1
BURTON ...E-5
CADILLAC ...D-4
CEDAR SPRINGS ...D-5
CHAMPION ...B-1
CHARLEVOIX ...D-3
CHARLOTTE ...D-5
CHEBOYGAN ...E-2
CLARE ...D-4
COPPER HARBOR ...B-1
COVINGTON ...B-1
CRYSTAL FALLS ...B-2
DEARBORN ...E-6
DETROIT ...F-6
DOUGLAS ...C-5
DUNDEE ...E-6
DURAND ...E-5
EASTPORT ...D-3
ELK RAPIDS ...D-3
ELMIRA ...D-3
ESCANABA ...C-2

FENTON ...E-5
FLINT ...E-5
GAYLORD ...E-3
GLADSTONE ...C-2
GRAND HAVEN ...C-5
GRAND RAPIDS ...D-5
HANCOCK ...B-1
HARBOR BEACH ...F-4
HARRISVILLE ...F-3
HASTINGS ...D-5
HILLMAN ...E-3
HOLLAND ...C-5
HOUGHTON ...B-1
HOUGHTON LAKE ...E-4
HOWARD CITY ...D-5
HURON BEACH ...F-3
IMLAY CITY ...F-5
IONIA ...D-5
IRON MOUNTAIN ...B-2
IRON RIVER ...B-2
IRONWOOD ...A-2
ISHPEMING ...B-2
JACKSON ...E-6
KALAMAZOO ...D-6
KALKASKA ...D-3
L'ANSE ...B-1
LANSING ...E-5
LEXINGTON ...F-5
LUDINGTON ...C-4
MACKINAW CITY ...E-2
MANCELONA ...D-3
MANISTEE ...C-4
MANISTIQUE ...C-2
MANTON ...D-4
MARLETTE ...F-5
MARQUETTE ...B-2
MARSHALL ...E-6
MASS CITY ...B-1
MENOMINEE ...C-3
MERRIWEATHER ...A-1
MUNISING ...C-2
MUSKEGON ...C-5
NEW BUFFALO ...C-6
NILES ...C-6
ONTONAGON ...A-1
OSCODA ...E-4
OWOSSO ...E-5
PETOSKEY ...D-3
PONTIAC ...E-5
PORT AUSTIN ...F-4
PORT HOPE ...F-4
PORT HURON ...F-5
PORT SANILAC ...F-4
PORTLAND ...D-5
POWERS ...B-2
RAPID RIVER ...C-2
REED CITY ...D-4
ROMEO ...E-5
SAGINAW ...E-5
SAULT STE. MARIE ...E-2
SCOTTVILLE ...C-4
SEBEWAING ...E-4
SHEPHERD ...D-4
SHINGLETON ...C-2
SOUTH HAVEN ...C-6
ST. IGNACE ...E-2
ST. JOHNS ...E-5
ST. JOSEPH ...C-6
STANDISH ...E-4
STURGIS ...D-6
TAWAS CITY ...E-4
THREE RIVERS ...D-6
TRAVERSE CITY ...D-3
TRENARY ...C-2
WAKEFIELD ...A-2
WATERSMEET ...A-2
WAYLAND ...D-5
WEST BRANCH ...E-4
YPSILANTI ...E-6

MINNESOTA
AITKIN ...C-4
ALBERT LEA ...C-6
ALEXANDRIA ...B-4
AUSTIN ...C-6
BAUDETTE ...B-1
BEMIDJI ...B-3
BENSON ...B-4
BIG FALLS ...B-2
BLACKDUCK ...B-2
BLOOMINGTON ...C-5
BLUE EARTH ...C-6

BRAINERD ...C-4
BRECKENRIDGE ...A-4
CAMBRIDGE ...C-4
CANBY ...A-5
CANNON FALLS ...C-5
CARLTON ...C-3
CENTER CITY ...C-5
CHASKA ...C-5
CHISHOLM ...C-2
CLOQUET ...C-3
COOK ...C-2
CROOKSTON ...A-2
CROSBY ...C-4
DETROIT LAKES ...B-3
DULUTH ...C-3
EAST GRAND FORKS ...A-2
ELBOW LAKE ...A-4
ELK RIVER ...C-4
FAIRMONT ...B-6
FERGUS FALLS ...A-4
FLOODWOOD ...C-3
FOSSTON ...B-2
GLENCOE ...C-5
GRAND MARAIS ...E-2
GRAND PORTAGE ...E-2
GRAND RAPIDS ...C-3
GRANITE FALLS ...A-5
GREENBUSH ...A-1
HALLOCK ...A-1
HAWLEY ...A-3
HIBBING ...C-3
HINCKLEY ...C-4
INTERNATIONAL FALLS ...C-1
JACKSON ...B-6
KARLSTAD ...A-1
LA CRESCENT ...D-6
LAKE BENTON ...A-5
LAKE CITY ...D-5
LITTLE FALLS ...C-4
LUVERNE ...A-6
MADELIA ...B-6
MAHNOMEN ...A-3
MANKATO ...C-5
MARSHALL ...B-5
MILACA ...C-4
MINNEAPOLIS ...C-5
MONTEVIDEO ...B-5
MOORHEAD ...A-3
MOOSE LAKE ...C-3
MORA ...C-4
NEWULM ...B-5
OLIVIA ...B-5
ONAMIA ...C-4
ORTONVILLE ...A-4
OWATONNA ...C-6
PARK RAPIDS ...B-3
PINE CITY ...C-4
PINE RIVER ...B-3
PIPESTONE ...A-6
PRESTON ...D-6
PRINCETON ...C-4
REDWING ...D-5
REDWOOD FALLS ...B-5
ROCHESTER ...D-6
ROSEAU ...B-1
SANDSTONE ...C-4
SAUK CENTRE ...B-4
SLEEPY EYE ...B-5
SPICER ...B-4
SPRING VALLEY ...D-6
SPRINGFIELD ...B-5
ST. CLOUD ...B-4
ST. JAMES ...B-6
ST. PAUL ...C-5
ST. PETER ...C-5
THIEF RIVER FALLS ...A-2
TRACY ...B-5
TWO HARBORS ...D-3
VIRGINIA ...D-2
WADENA ...B-3
WALKER ...B-3
WARREN ...A-2
WARROAD ...B-1
WASECA ...C-6
WILLMAR ...B-5
WORTHINGTON ...B-6

MISSISSIPPI
ABERDEEN ...D-2
AMORY ...D-2

BALDWYN ...D-1
BATESVILLE ...C-1
BAY SAINT LOUIS ...C-7
BEAUMONT ...D-6
BELZONI ...B-3
BILOXI ...D-7
BOONEVILLE ...D-1
BROOKHAVEN ...B-5
CANTON ...C-4
CLARKSDALE ...B-2
CLEVELAND ...B-3
CLINTON ...B-5
COLLINS ...C-6
COLUMBIA ...C-6
COLUMBUS ...D-3
CORINTH ...D-1
CRYSTAL SPRINGS ...B-5
ELLISVILLE ...C-5
EUPORA ...C-2
FAYETTE ...A-5
FLORA ...B-4
GREENVILLE ...A-3
GREENWOOD ...B-3
GRENADA ...C-2
GULFPORT ...D-7
HATTIESBURG ...D-6
HAZLEHURST ...B-5
HERNANDO ...B-1
HOLLANDALE ...A-4
HOLLY SPRINGS ...C-1
HORN LAKE ...B-1
INDIANOLA ...B-3
JACKSON ...C-4
LAUDERDALE ...D-4
LAUREL ...D-5
LELAND ...B-3
LOUISVILLE ...C-3
LUCEDALE ...D-6
LUMBERTON ...C-6
MACON ...D-3
MADISON ...C-4
MAGNOLIA ...B-6
MARKS ...B-2
MATHISTON ...D-3
MCCOMB ...B-6
MEADVILLE ...B-6
MENDENHALL ...C-5
MERIDIAN ...D-4
MONTICELLO ...B-6
MOUNT OLIVE ...C-5
NATCHEZ ...A-6
NEW ALBANY ...D-1
NEWTON ...D-5
OAKLAND ...C-2
OKOLONA ...D-2
OXFORD ...C-2
PASCAGOULA ...D-7
PICAYUNE ...C-7
PONTOTOC ...D-2
POPLARVILLE ...C-6
PORT GIBSON ...B-5
PRENTISS ...C-5
PURVIS ...C-6
QUITMAN ...D-5
REDWOOD ...B-4
ROLLING FORK ...B-4
RULEVILLE ...B-3
SENATOBIA ...B-1
STARKVILLE ...D-3
STATE LINE ...D-6
TCHULA ...B-3
TUNICA ...B-1
TUPELO ...D-1
TUTWILER ...B-2
TYLERTOWN ...C-6
VAIDEN ...C-3
VICKSBURG ...B-5
WALNUT ...D-1
WAYNESBORO ...D-5
WEST POINT ...D-3
WIGGINS ...D-7
WINONA ...C-3
WOODVILLE ...A-6
YAZOO CITY ...B-4

MISSOURI
ALBANY ...B-1
ALTON ...D-5
ANDERSON ...B-5
BETHANY ...B-1
BOLIVAR ...C-4
BOONVILLE ...C-2
BOWLING GREEN ...D-2
BRANSON ...C-5
BUFFALO ...C-4

CABOOL ...D-4
CAMDENTON ...C-3
CAMPBELL ...F-5
CAPE GIRARDEAU ...F-4
CARROLLTON ...B-2
CARTHAGE ...B-4
CHILLICOTHE ...C-2
CLINTON ...B-3
COLUMBIA ...C-2
CONCORDIA ...B-2
CUBA ...D-3
DEXTER ...F-5
DONIPHAN ...E-5
EL DORADO SPRINGS ...B-4
ELDON ...C-3
FARMINGTON ...E-3
FESTUS ...E-3
FREDERICKTOWN ...E-4
FULTON ...D-3
GRANT CITY ...B-1
GREENFIELD ...B-4
HAMILTON ...B-2
HANNIBAL ...D-2
HARRISONVILLE ...B-3
HOUSTON ...D-4
INDEPENDENCE ...B-2
JACKSON ...C-4
JEFFERSON CITY ...D-3
JOPLIN ...B-5
KAHOKA ...D-1
KANSAS CITY ...B-2
KENNETT ...F-5
KING CITY ...B-1
KIRKSVILLE ...C-1
LAMAR ...B-4
LINN ...D-3
MACON ...C-2
MALDEN ...E-5
MANSFIELD ...D-4
MARSHALL ...C-2
MARYVILLE ...B-1
MEMPHIS ...D-1
MEXICO ...D-2
MOBERLY ...C-2
MONETT ...B-5
MONROE CITY ...D-2
NEOSHO ...B-5
NEVADA ...B-4
NEW LONDON ...D-2
NEW MADRID ...F-5
OSCEOLA ...C-3
OZARK ...C-5
PARIS ...D-2
PERRYVILLE ...E-4
POPLAR BLUFF ...E-5
POTOSI ...E-4
PRINCETON ...C-1
RICH HILL ...B-4
ROCK PORT ...A-1
ROLLA ...D-4
SEDALIA ...C-3
SIKESTON ...F-5
SPRINGFIELD ...C-4
ST. CHARLES ...E-3
ST. JAMES ...E-3
ST. JOSEPH ...B-2
ST. LOUIS ...E-3
STANBERRY ...B-1
SWEET SPRINGS ...C-3
THAYER ...D-5
TIPTON ...C-3
TRENTON ...C-1
TROY ...E-2
UNIONVILLE ...C-1
VANDALIA ...D-2
VIENNA ...D-3
WARRENSBURG ...B-3
WARSAW ...C-3
WAYNESVILLE ...C-4
WENTZVILLE ...E-3
WEST PLAINS ...D-5
WILLOW SPRINGS ...D-5

MONTANA
ALZADA ...G-4
ANACONDA ...C-3
ASHLAND ...F-4
BAKER ...G-3
BARBER ...E-3
BELT ...C-2
BIG SANDY ...D-1
BIG TIMBER ...D-3
BILLINGS ...E-3
BOULDER ...C-3

BOZEMAN ...C-4
BRIDGER ...E-4
BROADUS ...G-4
BROADVIEW ...D-3
BROWNING ...B-1
BUTTE ...C-3
CASCADE ...C-2
CHESTER ...C-1
CHINOOK ...D-1
CHOTEAU ...C-2
CIRCLE ...F-2
COLUMBUS ...D-4
CONRAD ...C-1
CRAIG ...C-2
CULBERTSON ...G-1
CUT BANK ...C-1
DARBY ...B-3
DEER LODGE ...B-3
DELL ...B-4
DILLON ...B-4
DIVIDE ...B-3
DODSON ...E-1
DUTTON ...C-2
EAST HELENA ...C-3
EDGAR ...E-4
EUREKA ...A-1
EVERGREEN ...B-1
FALLON ...G-2
FORSYTH ...F-3
FORT BENTON ...D-2
FORTINE ...A-1
FRAZER ...F-2
FROMBERG ...E-4
GARRYOWEN ...E-4
GLASGOW ...F-1
GLEN ...B-4
GLENDIVE ...G-2
GREAT FALLS ...C-2
HAMILTON ...B-3
HAMMOND ...G-4
HARDIN ...E-3
HARLEM ...E-1
HARLOWTON ...D-3
HAVRE ...D-1
HELENA ...B-3
HINGHAM ...D-1
HINSDALE ...F-1
HOBSON ...D-2
HYSHAM ...E-3
JORDAN ...F-2
JUDITH GAP ...D-3
KALISPELL ...A-1
KINSEY ...F-2
KIOWA ...B-1
LAME DEER ...F-3
LAREDO ...D-1
LAUREL ...D-3
LEWISTOWN ...D-2
LIMA ...B-4
LINCOLN ...B-2
LINDSAY ...G-2
LIVINGSTON ...D-4
LODGE GRASS ...F-4
LOMA ...D-2
MALTA ...E-1
MANHATTAN ...C-3
MILES CITY ...F-3
MINER ...C-4
MISSOULA ...B-2
MOSBY ...E-2
NASHUA ...F-2
OLNEY ...A-1
PLEVNA ...G-3
POLSON ...A-2
POPLAR ...G-1
RED LODGE ...D-4
ROUNDUP ...E-3
SACO ...E-1
SHELBY ...C-1
ST. IGNATIUS ...A-2
STANFORD ...D-2
SULA ...B-3
SUNBURST ...C-1
TERRY ...F-3
TOWNSEND ...C-3
TROY ...A-1
WEST YELLOWSTONE ...C-4
WHITEFISH ...A-1
WIBAUX ...G-2
WINNETT ...E-2
WOLF POINT ...F-2
ZURICH ...D-1

Places Index

NEBRASKA

AINSWORTH D-2
ALLIANCE B-2
ALMA D-4
ANSELMO D-3
ANSLEY D-3
ARAPAHOE D-4
ATKINSON D-2
AUBURN G-4
BARTLETT E-2
BASSETT D-2
BATTLE CREEK F-2
BAYARD A-2
BEATRICE F-4
BELLEVUE G-3
BLAIR G-2
BLUE HILL E-4
BRIDGEPORT A-2
BROKEN BOW D-3
CAMBRIDGE C-4
CERESCO F-3
CHADRON A-1
CODY C-1
COLUMBUS F-3
CRAWFORD A-1
CRETE F-3
CROFTON F-1
CULBERTSON C-4
DALTON B-2
DALTON A-3
DONIPHAN E-3
DUNNING D-2
ELWOOD D-4
FAIRBURY F-4
FAIRMONT F-3
FRANKLIN D-4
FREMONT F-3
FRIEND F-4
GENEVA F-4
GORDON B-1
GRAND ISLAND E-3
GREELEY E-3
HAIGLER C-5
HARRISON A-1
HASTINGS E-4
HAY SPRINGS B-1
HEBRON F-4
HOLDREGE D-4
HUMPHREY F-2
HYANNIS B-2
IMPERIAL C-4
KIMBALL A-3
LEWELLEN B-3
LINCOLN F-3
LONG PINE D-2
LYONS F-2
MADISON E-2
MAYWOOD C-4
MCCOOK C-4
MERRIMAN B-1
MINDEN E-4
MITCHELL A-2
MORRILL A-2
MULLEN C-2
NEBRASKA CITY G-3
NELIGH E-2
NORFOLK F-2
NORTH BEND F-3
NORTH PLATTE C-3
OGALLALA B-3
OMAHA G-3
O'NEILL E-2
OSCEOLA B-3
OSHKOSH B-3
PALISADE C-4
PAPILLION G-3
PLAINVIEW E-2
PLATTSMOUTH G-3
RANDOLPH F-2
RAVENNA D-3
RED CLOUD E-4
RUSHVILLE B-1
S. SIOUX CITY G-2
SARGENT D-2
SCHUYLER F-3
SCOTTSBLUFF A-2
SIDNEY A-3
SPENCER D-1
SPRINGVIEW D-1
ST. PAUL E-3
STAPLETON C-3
STROMSBURG F-3
STUART D-1
SUTTON E-4
TAYLOR D-2

TECUMSEH F-4
THEDFORD C-2
TRENTON C-4
VALENTINE C-1
WAHOO F-3
WAUNETA C-4
WELLFLEET F-3
WINNEBAGO F-2
WISNER F-2
WOOD LAKE D-1
WYMORE F-4
YORK F-3

NEVADA

AMARGOSA VALLEY C-6
ASH SPRINGS D-5
AUSTIN C-3
BASALT B-4
BATTLE MOUNTAIN...C-2
BEATTY C-6
CALIENTE D-5
CARLIN C-2
CARSON CITY A-4
COALDALE C-4
CURRANT D-4
CURRIE D-3
ELKO D-2
ELY D-3
EUREKA C-3
FALLON B-3
FERNLEY A-3
GLENDALE D-6
GOLCONDA B-2
GOLDFIELD C-5
HALLECK D-2
HAWTHORNE A-4
HENDERSON D-6
JACKPOT D-1
LAGES D-3
LAS VEGAS C-6
LAUGHLIN D-7
LOVELOCK B-3
LUNING B-4
MCDERMITT B-1
MESQUITE D-6
MIDDLEGATE B-3
MILL CITY B-2
NORTH LAS VEGAS ...D-6
OREANA B-2
OROVADA B-1
PANACA D-5
PIOCHE D-5
RENO A-3
SCHURZ A-4
SCOTTY'S JUNCTION..C-5
SILVER SPRINGS A-3
SPARKS A-3
TONOPAH C-5
TOPAZ LAKE A-4
WARM SPRINGS C-4
WELLS D-2
WEST WENDOVER D-2
WILKINS D-1
WINNEMUCCA B-2

NEW HAMPSHIRE

ALTON C-5
ANTRIM B-6
COLEBROOK C-2
CONCORD B-6
CONWAY C-4
ERROL C-2
GLEN C-3
GORHAM C-3
HILLSBORO B-6
JAFFREY B-7
KEENE A-7
LANCASTER C-3
LITTLETON B-3
MANCHESTER C-6
MEREDITH B-5
NASHUA C-7
NORTH STRATFORD..C-2
NORTHWOOD C-6
PORTSMOUTH D-6
ROCHESTER C-6
STEWARTSTOWN C-2
TROY A-7
TWIN MOUNTAIN C-3
UNION C-5
WEST OSSIPEE C-4
WOODSVILLE B-4

NEW JERSEY

ANDOVER B-2

ASBURY PARK..........D-4
ATLANTIC CITY C-6
BELMAR D-4
BERLIN B-5
BORDENTOWN C-4
BRIGANTINE C-6
BURLINGTON B-4
BUTLER C-2
CAMDEN B-4
CAPE MAY B-7
CHERRY HILL B-4
CHESTER B-2
DENNISVILLE B-7
EAST ORANGE D-2
EDISON C-3
ELIZABETH D-2
ELMER A-6
FAIRFIELD C-2
FRANKLIN C-1
FREEHOLD C-4
HACKENSACK D-2
HAINESVILLE B-1
HAMMONTON B-5
HEDGER HOUSE B-5
HIGHLANDS D-3
INDIAN MILLS B-5
JERSEY CITY D-2
LAKEWOOD C-4
LONG BRANCH D-4
MANALAPAN C-4
MANASQUAN D-4
MARLTON B-5
MAYS LANDING B-6
NETCONG B-2
NEW BRUNSWICK B-3
NEWARK C-2
NEWTON B-1
NORTH CAPE MAY B-7
OCEAN CITY C-6
PARAMUS D-2
PASSAIC D-2
PATERSON C-2
PERTH AMBOY C-3
PHILLIPSBURG B-2
PLAINFIELD C-3
POINT PLEASANT D-4
PORT MONMOUTH ...D-3
PRINCETON B-3
RAMSEY D-1
RED BANK D-3
SEASIDE HEIGHTS D-4
SHIP BOTTOM C-5
SILVERTON D-4
SOMERVILLE C-3
SOUTH RIVER C-3
SPARTA C-1
TOMS RIVER C-4
TRENTON B-4
UNION C-2
WOODSTOWN A-5

NEW MEXICO

ABBOTT D-2
ABIQUIU C-2
ALAMOGORDO C-5
ALBUQUERQUE B-3
ALMA A-4
ANTHONY B-6
ARTESIA D-5
AZTEC B-1
BELEN B-3
BERNALILLO B-2
BERNARDO B-2
BINGHAM C-4
BLOOMFIELD B-1
BUCKHORN A-5
CABALLO B-5
CAPITAN C-4
CAPROCK E-4
CARLSBAD D-5
CARRIZOZO C-4
CASA BLANCA B-3
CIMARRON D-1
CLAYTON E-1
CLINES CORNERS C-3
CLOVIS E-3
CORONA C-3
CUBA B-2
DATIL A-4
DEMING A-5
DILIA D-3
DURAN C-4
EAGLE NEST C-1
ELIDA E-4
ELK D-5

ELKINS E-4
ENCINO C-3
ESPANOLA C-2
FARMINGTON A-1
FORT SUMNER D-3
GALLUP A-2
GRANTS A-3
HATCH B-5
HOBBS E-5
HONDO C-4
HOPE D-5
HURLEY A-5
LAS CRUCES B-5
LAS VEGAS C-2
LOGAN D-3
LORDSBURG A-5
LOS LUNAS C-3
LOVINGTON E-5
MAGDALENA B-4
MALAGA E-5
MAXWELL D-1
MORIARTY C-3
MOUNTAINAIR C-3
NADINE E-5
NAGEEZI B-2
NARA VISA E-2
NASCHITTI A-2
NEWKIRK D-3
ORGAN B-5
OROGRANDE C-5
OSCURRO C-4
PIE TOWN A-3
POJOAQUE C-2
PORTALES E-4
QUEMADO A-3
RAMON D-4
RATON D-1
RIBERA C-2
RODEO A-6
ROSWELL D-4
SAN ACACIA B-3
SANANTONIO B-4
SAN JON E-3
SANTA FE C-2
SANTA ROSA D-3
SEPAR A-5
SEVEN RIVERS D-5
SHIPROCK A-1
SILVER CITY A-5
SOCORRO B-4
SPRINGER D-2
TAOS C-2
TATUM E-4
TIERRA AMARILLA B-1
TRUTH OR
  CONSEQUENCES B-4
TUCUMCARI D-3
TULAROSA C-5
VAUGHN D-3
WAGON MOUND D-2
WATROUS D-2
WHITES CITY D-5
WILLARD C-3
YESO D-3
ZUNI PUEBLO A-3

NEW YORK

ADAMS D-2
ALBANY E-3
ALDER CREEK D-3
ALEXANDRIA BAY C-1
AMENIA F-4
AMSTERDAM E-3
ANDES E-4
ANTWERP D-2
AUBURN C-4
BATH C-4
BEACON F-5
BINGHAMTON D-4
BUFFALO A-3
CAIRO E-4
CANTON D-1
CAPE VINCENT D-2
CATSKILL F-4
CAZENOVIA D-3
CHATEAUGAY E-1
CHEEKTOWAGA B-3
CORNING C-4
CORTLAND D-4
DANSVILLE B-4
DELHI E-4
DEPOSIT D-4

DRESDEN C-3
DRYDEN D-4
DUNKIRK A-4
EAST HAMPTON G-5
EAST ISLIP F-6
ELLICOTTVILLE A-4
ELMIRA C-4
ESPERANCE E-3
FINE E-1
FLEISCHMANNS E-4
FRANKLINVILLE B-4
FREDONIA A-4
FULTON C-3
GENESEO B-3
GENEVA C-3
GOUVERNEUR D-1
GOWANDA A-4
GREAT NECK F-6
GREECE B-3
GREENE D-4
GREENPORT G-5
HAMBURG A-3
HAMPTON BAYS G-5
HANCOCK D-4
HARRISVILLE D-2
HARTWICK D-3
HERKIMER E-3
HICKSVILLE F-6
HORNELL B-4
HUDSON FALLS F-3
HUNTINGTON
  STATION F-5
ILION D-3
INDIAN LAKE E-2
ITHACA C-4
JAMESTOWN A-4
KINGSTON F-4
LAKE CLEAR
  JUNCTION E-1
LAKE GEORGE E-2
LAKE PLACID F-1
LIBERTY E-4
LIMA B-3
LIMESTONE A-4
LOCKPORT B-3
LONG BEACH F-6
LONG LAKE E-2
LOWVILLE D-2
LYONS C-3
LYONS FALLS D-2
MALONE E-1
MASSENA E-1
MASTIC BEACH G-6
MATTITUCK G-5
MAYVILLE A-4
MECHANICVILLE E-3
MONTAUK G-5
MONTICELLO E-5
MORRISTOWN D-1
NASSAU F-3
NEWCITY F-5
NEW YORK F-6
NEWARK C-3
NEWBURGH E-5
NIAGARA FALLS A-3
NORWICH D-4
OGDENSBURG D-1
OLCOTT B-3
OLD FORGE E-2
OLEAN B-4
ONEONTA D-4
OSWEGO C-2
OWEGO C-4
PASSAIC E-5
PEEKSKILL F-5
PHOENICIA E-4
PLATTSBURGH F-1
PORT JEFFERSON F-5
POTSDAM E-1
POUGHKEEPSIE F-5
PRATTSVILLE E-4
PULASKI D-2
RIVERHEAD G-5
ROCHESTER C-3
ROCKY PT F-5
ROME D-3
ROSCOE E-4
SACKETS HARBOR....C-2
SALAMANCA A-4
SARATOGA SPRINGS..E-3
SCHENECTADY F-3
SHERMAN A-4

SILVER CREEK A-3
SODUS C-3
SOMERVILLE E-6
SPECULATOR E-2
SYRACUSE C-3
TROY F-3
TUPPER LAKE E-2
UTICA D-3
WADDINGTON D-1
WARSAW B-3
WATERTOWN D-2
WATERVILLE D-3
WATKINS GLEN C-4
WELLSVILLE B-4
WESTFIELD A-4
WHITE PLAINS F-5
WHITEHALL F-2
WILSON B-3
WINDSOR F-2
WINSTON-SALEM D-3
WINTON F-1

NORTH CAROLINA

ALBEMARLE D-2
ASHEBORO D-2
ASHEVILLE B-2
ATLANTIC G-3
BLACK MOUNTAIN ...B-2
BOONE B-2
BREVARD B-2
BRYSON CITY A-2
BURGAW E-3
BURLINGTON D-2
BUXTON G-2
CAROLINA BEACH F-4
CARTHAGE D-2
CARY E-2
CHARLOTTE C-2
CLINTON E-3
COLUMBIA G-2
CONCORD C-2
DUNN E-2
DURHAM E-2
EDENTON F-2
ELIZABETH CITY F-1
ELIZABETHTOWN E-3
FAYETTEVILLE D-3
FOREST CITY B-2
FRANKLIN A-2
GASTONIA C-2
GOLDSBORO E-2
GREENSBORO D-2
GREENVILLE F-2
HAMLET D-3
HATTERAS G-2
HAVELOCK F-3
HENDERSON E-1
HENDERSONVILLE B-2
HICKORY C-2
HIGH POINT D-2
JACKSONVILLE F-3
JEFFERSON C-1
KANNAPOLIS C-2
KINSTON E-2
KITTY HAWK G-2
LAURINBURG D-3
LENOIR C-2
LEXINGTON C-2
LOUISBURG E-2
LUMBERTON E-3
MADISON D-1
MAIDEN C-2
MANTEO G-2
MONROE C-3
MOREHEAD CITY F-3
MORGANTON B-2
MOUNT AIRY C-1
MOUNT OLIVE E-2
MURPHY A-2
NEW BERN F-2
NEWTON C-2
OCRACOKE G-3
OCRACOKE G-3
OXFORD E-1
PINEHURST D-2
PLYMOUTH F-2
RALEIGH E-2
REIDSVILLE D-1
RICHLANDS E-3
ROANOKE RAPIDS....E-1
ROBBINSVILLE A-2
ROCKY MOUNT F-2
ROXBORO E-1
SALISBURY C-2
SALVO G-2
SANFORD E-2
SHALLOTTE E-4

SILER CITY D-2
SMITHFIELD E-2
SNOW HILL E-2
SUNSET BEACH E-4
SWANQUARTER G-2
SYLVA B-2
TABOR CITY E-4
TOPSAIL BEACH F-3
VANCEBORO F-2
WADESBORO D-3
WARSAW E-3
WASHINGTON F-2
WAYNESVILLE B-2
WHITEVILLE E-3
WILKESBORO C-1
WILLIAMSTON F-2
WILMINGTON E-3
WILSON E-2
WINDSOR F-2
WINSTON-SALEM D-3
WINTON F-1

NORTH DAKOTA

ALEXANDER A-2
AMIDON A-4
ANAMOOSE C-2
BALFOUR D-2
BEACH A-3
BELFIELD B-3
BERTHOLD C-2
BISMARCK D-3
BOTTINEAU D-1
BOWBELLS B-1
BOWMAN A-4
CANDO E-1
CARRINGTON E-3
CAVALIER F-1
CHURCHS FERRY E-2
COLEHARBOR C-2
COLFAX G-4
CROSBY A-1
DEVILS LAKE E-2
DICKINSON B-3
DRAKE D-2
DRAYTON F-1
DUNSEITH D-1
EDGELEY E-4
ELLENDALE E-4
FARGO G-3
FESSENDEN E-2
FORTUNA A-1
GARDNER G-3
GLADSTONE B-3
GRAND FORKS G-2
GRANVILLE C-2
GREAT BEND G-4
HAVANA F-4
HAZELTON D-4
HETTINGER B-4
HORACE G-3
JAMESTOWN E-3
KENMARE B-1
KNOX E-1
LAKOTA F-2
LANGDON F-1
LEEDS E-2
LINTON D-4
MANDAN D-3
MANVEL G-2
MARMARTH A-4
MEDINA E-3
MEDORA A-3
MINNEWAUKAN E-2
MINOT C-2
MOHALL C-1
MONANGO E-4
NECHE F-1
NEW ROCKFORD E-2
NEW SALEM C-3
NOONAN B-1
PEMBINA F-1
PETERSBURG F-2
RAY B-1
REYNOLDS G-2
RICHARDTON B-3
ROCKLAKE E-1
ROLLA F-1
ROSS B-2
SAWYER D-2
SCRANTON B-4
STANLEY B-2
STEELE E-4
STRASBURG D-4
TOLLEY C-1
TOWNER D-1

OHIO

AKRON D-2
ANTWERP A-2
ASHLAND C-3
ASHTABULA E-1
ATHENS D-5
BELLEVUE C-2
BETHEL A-5
BOWLING GREEN B-2
BRYAN A-2
BUCYRUS C-3
CADIZ E-3
CALDWELL E-4
CAMBRIDGE D-4
CANTON D-3
CHILLICOTHE C-5
CINCINNATI A-5
CIRCLEVILLE C-4
CLEVELAND D-1
CLYDE C-2
COLUMBUS C-4
CONNEAUT E-1
CORTLAND D-2
COSHOCTON D-3
DAYTON A-4
DEFIANCE A-2
DELAWARE B-4
DELPHOS A-3
DOVER E-3
EAST LIVERPOOL E-3
EATON A-4
ELYRIA D-2
EUCLID D-1
FINDLAY B-2
FOSTORIA B-3
FRANKLIN A-5
FREMONT B-2
GALION C-3
GALLIPOLIS D-6
GREENVILLE A-4
HAMILTON A-5
HILLSBORO B-5
JACKSON C-5
KENT E-2
KENTON B-3
LANCASTER C-4
LIMA B-3
LISBON E-2
LODI D-2
LOGAN C-5
LORAIN D-1
MANSFIELD C-3
MARIETTA D-5
MARION C-4
MARTINS FERRY F-4
MARYSVILLE B-4
MASSILLON D-3
MAUMEE B-2
MECHANICSBURG B-4
MILFORD A-5
MILLERSBURG D-3
MINERVA E-3
MOUNT STERLING ...C-4
MOUNT VERNON C-4
NAPOLEON A-2
NEW PHILADELPHIA..D-3
NEWARK C-4
NEWCOMERSTOWN..D-3
NORWALK C-2
OTTAWA A-3
PAINESVILLE D-1
PEEBLES B-5
PIQUA A-4
POMEROY D-6
PORT CLINTON C-2
PORTSMOUTH C-6
RAVENNA E-2
RIPLEY B-6
SALEM E-2
SANDUSKY C-2
SIDNEY B-4
SOMERSET D-4
SOUTH POINT D-6
SPRINGFIELD B-4
ST. CLAIRSVILLE E-4
ST. MARYS A-3

60

TEUBENVILLE....E-3
OLEDO....B-1
ROY....B-4
HRICHSVILLE....E-3
PPER SANDUSKY....C-2
RBANA....B-4
TICA....D-3
AN WERT....A-2
WAPAKONETA....B-3
ARREN....E-2
ASHINGTON COURT
  HOUSE....B-5
WAVERLY....C-5
ILLARD....C-2
ILMINGTON....B-5
OODVILLE....B-1
ENIA....E-3
OUNGSTOWN....E-2
ANESVILLE....D-4

OKLAHOMA

DA....F-3
LTUS....
LVA....D-1
NADARKO....D-3
NTLERS....G-4
PACHE....D-3
RDMORE....E-4
RNETT....F-4
TOKA....
ARTLESVILLE....
LACKWELL....E-1
OISE CITY....A-1
OSWELL....
RIDGEPORT....D-2
RISTOW....F-2
ROKEN ARROW....
ROKEN BOW....G-4
UFFALO....F-1
URBANK....F-1
ADDO....F-4
ALVIN....
HANDLER....E-2
HECOTAH....
HEROKEE....D-1
HEYENNE....C-2
HICKASHA....D-3
LAREMORE....F-2
AYTON....
EO SPRINGS....D-1
LINTON....D-2
OALGATE....F-3
OLBERT....F-4
ORDELL....D-3
USHING....
AVIDSON....D-4
OVER....
UKE....C-3
UNCAN....E-3
URANT....
OMOND....E-2
  RENO....D-3
GIN....D-3
K CITY....C-3
ID....
UFAULA....F-3
IRVIEW....D-2
ORGAN....
RT SUPPLY....C-1
EDERICK....D-4
EARY....
UTHRIE....E-2
YMON....
ARDESTY....G-3
RTSHORNE....G-3
AVENER....
NRYETTA....F-2
OLDENVILLE....F-3
OLLIS....
UGO....G-4
ABEL....
W....G-2
ANSAS....
NGFISHER....E-2
NGSTON....F-4
WTON....D-3
ANGUM....
ARIETTA....E-4
ARLOW....
AY....C-1
CALESTER....
EDFORD....E-1
AMI....G-1
USKOGEE....
ASH....D-1
RMAN....E-3

NOWATA....F-1
OKLAHOMA CITY....E-2
OKMULGEE....F-2
ORLANDO....E-2
PAULS VALLEY....E-3
PAWHUSKA....F-1
PAWNEE....E-2
PERRY....E-2
PONCA CITY....E-1
POND CREEK....E-1
POTEAU....G-3
PRYOR CREEK....G-2
PURCELL....E-3
RANDLETT....D-4
RATLIFF CITY....E-4
ROOSEVELT....D-3
ROSSTON....C-1
SALLISAW....G-2
SAPULPA....F-2
SAYRE....C-3
SEILING....D-2
SEMINOLE....E-3
SHAWNEE....E-3
SMITHVILLE....G-3
SNYDER....D-3
STILLWATER....E-2
STILWELL....G-2
STROUD....E-2
SULPHUR....E-3
TAHLEQUAH....G-2
TALOGA....D-2
TEXHOMA....A-1
TEXOLA....C-3
TULSA....F-2
VINITA....G-1
WATONGA....D-2
WAURIKA....E-4
WAYNOKA....D-1
WEATHERFORD....D-3
WESTVILLE....G-2
WETUMKA....F-3
WILBURTON....G-3
WOODWARD....C-2

OREGON

ALB ANY....B-2
ARLINGTON....D-1
ASHLAND....B-5
ASTORIA....B-1
BAKER....F-2
BANDON....A-4
BEAVERTON....B-1
BEND....D-3
BLY....D-5
BOARDMAN....E-1
BROOKINGS....A-5
BURNS....E-3
BURNS JUNCTION....F-4
CANNON BEACH....B-1
CANYON CITY....E-3
CAVE JUNCTION....A-5
CHILOQUIN....C-4
COBURG....B-3
COOS BAY....B-4
COQUILLE....B-4
CORVALLIS....B-2
COTTAGE GROVE....B-3
DAYVILLE....D-2
DEPOE BAY....A-2
DETROIT....C-2
DUNES CITY....A-3
EUGENE....B-3
FLORENCE....A-3
GOLD BEACH....A-4
GRANTS PASS....B-4
GRASS VALLEY....D-2
GRESHAM....C-1
HARBOR....A-5
HILLSBORO....B-1
HOOD RIVER....C-1
HUNTINGTON....G-3
IDANHA....C-2
JORDAN VALLEY....F-4
KLAMATH FALLS....C-5
LA GRANDE....F-2
LAPINE....C-4
LAKEVIEW....D-5
LEBANON....C-2
LINCOLN BEACH....A-2
LINCOLN CITY....B-2
LONG CREEK....E-2
LOWELL....C-3
MADRAS....D-2
MAUPIN....D-2
MCDERMITT....F-5
MCMINNVILLE....B-2

MEDFORD....B-5
MILL CITY....C-2
MITCHELL....D-2
NEWBERG....B-2
NEWPORT....A-2
NORTH BEND....B-3
NORTH POWDER....F-2
NYSSA....G-3
OAKRIDGE....C-3
ONTARIO....G-3
PENDLETON....E-1
PILOT ROCK....E-2
PORT ORFORD....A-4
PORTLAND....C-1
PRAIRIE CITY....E-2
PRINEVILLE....D-3
RAINIER....B-1
REDMOND....D-3
REEDSPORT....B-3
RHODODENDRON....C-2
RILEY....E-3
ROCKAWAY BEACH....B-1
SALEM....B-2
SEASIDE....B-1
SENECA....E-3
SHANIKO....D-2
SISTERS....C-3
SPRINGFIELD....B-3
ST. HELENS....C-1
SWEET HOME....B-3
TALENT....B-5
THE DALLES....D-1
TILLAMOOK....B-1
UKIAH....E-2
UNITY....F-2
VALE....F-2
WALDPORT....B-2
WASCO....D-1
WESTON....F-1
WINSTON....B-4
YACHATS....A-3

PENNSYLVANIA

ALLENTOWN....F-3
ALTOONA....C-4
BARNSBORO....C-3
BEAVER....A-3
BEDFORD....C-4
BERWICK....E-3
BETHEL PARK....A-4
BETHLEHEM....G-3
BLAIRSVILLE....B-4
BLAKELY....F-2
BLOOMSBURG....E-3
BROOKVILLE....B-2
CALIFORNIA....A-4
CANONSBURG....A-4
CARLISLE....E-4
CHAMBERSBURG....D-4
CHESTER....F-4
CLARION....B-2
CLEARFIELD....C-3
CORRY....B-1
COUDERSPORT....D-2
DANVILLE....E-3
DILLSBURG....E-4
DOYLESTOWN....G-4
DRIFTWOOD....C-2
DUBOIS....C-3
DUSHORE....E-2
EASTON....G-3
EBENSBURG....B-4
EDINBORO....A-1
EMMAUS....F-4
EMPORIUM....C-2
ERIE....A-1
FRANKLIN....A-2
FREDERICKSBURG....F-4
GALETON....D-2
GETTYSBURG....D-5
GIRARD....A-1
GREENSBURG....B-4
GREENVILLE....A-2
HARRISBURG....D-4
HAWLEY....G-2
HERSHEY....E-4
HOLLIDAYSBURG....C-4
HONESDALE....G-2
HUNTINGDON....D-4
INDIANA....B-3
JOHNSTOWN....B-4
KANE....C-2
KITTANNING....B-3
LANCASTER....E-4
LANSDALE....G-4
LAPORTE....E-2

LEBANON....E-4
LEHIGHTON....E-4
LEVITTOWN....G-4
LEWISBURG....E-3
LEWISTOWN....D-4
LIVERPOOL....E-3
LOCK HAVEN....D-3
MAHAFFEY....C-3
MANSFIELD....E-2
MCCANDLESS....A-4
MEADVILLE....A-2
MILFORD....G-3
MILTON....E-3
MONROEVILLE....B-4
MOUNT JOY....E-4
MOUNT UNION....D-4
MT. POCONO....G-3
MUNCY....E-2
NANTICOKE....F-2
NAZARETH....G-3
NEW BETHLEHEM....B-3
NEW CASTLE....A-3
NORRISTOWN....F-4
OIL CITY....A-2
PHILADELPHIA....G-4
PHILIPSBURG....C-3
PITTSBURGH....A-4
PORT MATILDA....C-3
POTTSTOWN....F-4
POTTSVILLE....F-3
PUNXSUTAWNEY....B-3
QUAKERTOWN....F-4
READING....F-4
RENOVO....D-2
RIDGWAY....C-2
SAYRE....E-1
SCRANTON....F-2
SELINSGROVE....E-3
SHAMOKIN....E-3
SHARON....A-2
SHEFFIELD....B-2
SHENANDOAH....E-3
SMETHPORT....C-1
ST. MARYS....C-2
STATE COLLEGE....D-3
SUNBURY....E-3
TAMAQUA....F-3
TIONESTA....B-2
TOWANDA....E-2
TROY....E-2
TUNKHANNOCK....F-2
UNION CITY....A-1
UNIONTOWN....A-4
WARREN....B-1
WASHINGTON....A-4
WAYNESBURG....A-4
WELLSBORO....D-2
WILKES-BARRE....F-2
WILLIAMSPORT....E-2
WINDBER....C-4
WYALUSING....F-2
YORK....E-4

RHODE ISLAND

CHEPACHET....B-2
CRANSTON....C-2
EAST GREENWICH....C-3
MIDDLETOWN....D-4
NARRAGANSETT
  PIER....D-4
NEWPORT....D-4
PAWTUCKET....C-2
PORTSMOUTH....D-3
PROVIDENCE....C-2
WARWICK....C-3
WEST WARWICK....B-3
WESTERLY....A-3
WOONSOCKET....C-1

SOUTH CAROLINA

ABBEVILLE....B-2
AIKEN....C-3
ANDERSON....B-3
BARNWELL....D-3
BEAUFORT....D-5
BENNETTSVILLE....E-2
CAMDEN....D-2
CHARLESTON....E-4
CHERAW....E-2
CHESTER....C-2
COLUMBIA....D-2

CONWAY....F-3
DILLON....E-2
FAIRFAX....C-4
FLORENCE....E-2
FURMAN....D-4
GEORGETOWN....F-3
GREENVILLE....B-1
GREENWOOD....B-2
HAMPTON....D-4
HILTON HEAD
  ISLAND....D-5
ISLE OF PALMS....E-4
JAMESTOWN....E-3
KERSHAW....D-2
LADSON....E-4
LAKE CITY....E-3
LANCASTER....D-2
LAURENS....C-2
LORIS....F-2
MANNING....E-3
MARION....F-2
MCCORMICK....B-3
MYRTLE BEACH....F-3
NEWBERRY....C-2
NORTH....D-3
ORANGEBURG....D-3
PORT ROYAL....D-5
RED BANK....D-3
ROCK HILL....C-1
SALUDA....C-2
SEABROOK ISLAND....E-4
SENECA....B-2
SPARTANBURG....C-1
ST. GEORGE....D-4
ST. MATTHEWS....D-3
SUMTER....D-3
TAYLORS....B-1
UNION....C-2
WALTERBORO....D-4
WHITMIRE....C-2
WINNSBORO....C-2
YORK....D-1

SOUTH DAKOTA

ABERDEEN....F-1
ALEXANDRIA....F-4
ARLINGTON....F-3
ARMOUR....F-4
ASHTON....F-2
BATESLAND....B-4
BELLE FOURCHE....A-2
BERESFORD....G-4
BLUNT....D-2
BOWDLE....E-1
BRISTOL....F-1
BROOKINGS....G-3
BUFFALO....A-1
BURKE....E-4
CANTON....G-4
COLOME....E-4
COTTONWOOD....C-3
CUSTER....A-3
DEADWOOD....A-2
DOLAND....F-2
DUPREE....C-2
EDGEMONT....A-4
ELK POINT....G-5
FAITH....B-2
FAULKTON....E-2
FRUITDALE....A-2
GETTYSBURG....D-2
GROTON....F-1
HAYES....C-3
HENRY....F-2
HIGHMORE....E-2
HILL CITY....A-3
HOT SPRINGS....A-4
HURON....F-3
IPSWICH....E-1
KADOKA....C-3
LA PLANT....C-2
LEAD....A-3
LEBANON....D-2
LEMMON....B-1
LUDLOW....A-1
MADISON....G-3
MARTIN....C-4
MAURINE....B-2
MCINTOSH....C-1
MCLAUGHLIN....D-1
MIDLAND....C-3
MILBANK....G-2

MILLER....E-2
MISSION....D-4
MITCHELL....F-3
MOBRIDGE....D-1
MOUND CITY....D-1
MUD BUTTE....B-2
MURDO....D-3
NEW EFFINGTON....G-1
NEWELL....A-2
OGLALA....B-4
OLIVET....F-4
PARADE....C-2
PHILIP....C-3
PIERRE....D-3
PINE RIDGE....B-4
PLANKINTON....E-3
PRINGLE....A-3
RAPID CITY....A-3
REDFIELD....E-2
REDIG....A-1
SALEM....F-3
SELBY....D-1
SIOUX FALLS....G-4
SPEARFISH....A-2
STAMFORD....C-3
STICKNEY....F-4
STURGIS....A-3
TILFORD....A-3
TYNDALL....F-4
VERMILLION....G-5
VETAL....D-4
WAGNER....F-4
WALL....B-3
WARNER....F-1
WATERTOWN....G-2
WAUBAY....F-1
WESSINGTON....E-3
WESTPORT....E-1
WHITE RIVER....D-4
WINNER....D-4
YANKTON....G-4

TENNESSEE

ALCOA....E-3
ATWOOD....B-2
BOLIVAR....B-3
BRISTOL....G-2
BROWNSVILLE....A-3
CHATTANOOGA....D-3
CHURCH HILL....G-2
CLARKSVILLE....C-2
CLEVELAND....E-3
COLUMBIA....C-3
COOKEVILLE....D-2
COVINGTON....A-3
CROSSVILLE....E-2
DAYTON....E-3
DICKSON....C-2
DUCKTOWN....E-3
DUNLAP....D-3
DYERSBURG....A-2
ELIZABETHTON....G-2
ERIN....C-2
FAYETTEVILLE....C-3
FRANKLIN....C-2
GREENEVILLE....F-2
HARRIMAN....E-2
HENDERSONVILLE....D-2
HUMBOLDT....B-3
HUNTINGDON....B-2
JACKSON....B-3
JAMESTOWN....E-2
JOHNSON CITY....G-2
KINGSPORT....G-2
KNOXVILLE....F-2
LA FOLLETTE....F-2
LAWRENCEBURG....C-3
LEBANON....D-2
LINDEN....C-3
LIVINGSTON....E-2
LORETTO....C-3
MANCHESTER....D-3
MARTIN....B-2
MARYVILLE....F-3
MCKENZIE....B-2
MCMINNVILLE....D-3
MEMPHIS....A-3
MILAN....B-2
MILLINGTON....A-3
MONTEAGLE....D-3
MORRISTOWN....F-2
MURFREESBORO....C-2
NASHVILLE....C-2
NEW MARKET....F-2
OAK RIDGE....E-2
ONEIDA....E-2

TEXAS

ABILENE....D-3
ALBANY....D-3
ALICE....E-6
ALPINE....B-4
AMARILLO....C-1
ANDREWS....B-3
ANGLETON....G-5
ANSON....C-3
ARANSAS PASS....F-6
ARLINGTON....E-3
ATHENS....E-3
AUSTIN....E-5
BALLINGER....D-4
BALMORHEA....B-4
BAY CITY....F-5
BAYTOWN....G-5
BEAUMONT....F-5
BEEVILLE....E-6
BIG LAKE....C-4
BIG SPRING....C-3
BOGATA....E-2
BOWIE....E-3
BRACKETTVILLE....D-5
BRADY....D-4
BRECKENRIDGE....E-3
BRENHAM....F-5
BROWNFIELD....B-3
BROWNSVILLE....E-7
BROWNWOOD....E-4
BRYAN....F-4
BUFFALO....F-4
BURLESON....E-3
BURNET....E-4
CAMERON....F-4
CANADIAN....D-1
CANYON....C-2
CARRIZO SPRINGS....D-6
CARTHAGE....F-3
CEDAR PARK....E-4
CENTER....F-3
CHANNING....C-1
CHILDRESS....D-2
CHRISTOVAL....D-4
CISCO....D-3
CLARENDON....D-2
CLEVELAND....G-5
CLUTE....G-5
COLEMAN....E-4
COLORADO CITY....D-3
COMANCHE....E-4
COMSTOCK....C-5
CONROE....F-5
CORPUS CHRISTI....F-6
CORRIGAN....G-4
CORSICANA....F-3
COTULLA....D-6
CROCKETT....F-4
CRYSTAL CITY....D-6
CUERO....E-5
DALHART....C-1
DALLAS....E-3
DECATUR....E-3
DEL RIO....D-5
DENISON....E-2
DENTON....F-3
DICKENS....C-2
DILLEY....E-6
DIMMITT....C-2
DRYDEN....C-5
DUMAS....C-1
EAGLE PASS....D-6
EDEN....D-4
EDINBURG....E-7
EDNA....F-5
EL PASO....A-3
ELDORADO....D-4
ENCINAL....D-6

ENCINO....E-7
FABENS....A-4
FALFURRIAS....E-6
FARWELL....C-2
FLOYDADA....C-2
FORT STOCKTON....B-4
FORT WORTH....E-3
FREDERICKSBURG....D-5
FREEPORT....G-5
FREER....E-6
FRIONA....C-2
GAINESVILLE....E-3
GALVESTON....G-5
GATESVILLE....E-4
GEORGE WEST....E-6
GIDDINGS....F-5
GOLDTHWAITE....E-4
GOLIAD....E-6
GREENVILLE....F-3
GUTHRIE....D-3
HARLINGEN....E-7
HASKELL....D-3
HEARNE....F-4
HEMPSTEAD....F-5
HENDERSON....G-3
HENRIETTA....E-2
HEREFORD....C-2
HEWITT....E-4
HICO....E-4
HILLSBORO....E-4
HONDO....D-5
HOUSTON....F-5
HUNTSVILLE....F-4
JACKSBORO....E-3
JACKSONVILLE....F-4
JASPER....G-4
JEFFERSON....G-3
JOHNSON CITY....E-5
JUNCTION....D-4
KATY....F-5
KENEDY....E-6
KERMIT....B-4
KERRVILLE....D-5
KILGORE....F-3
KILLEEN....E-4
KINGSVILLE....E-6
LA GRANGE....F-5
LAMESA....C-3
LAMPASAS....E-4
LAREDO....D-6
LEAKEY....D-5
LEVELLAND....C-3
LITTLEFIELD....C-2
LIVINGSTON....G-4
LONGVIEW....G-3
LUBBOCK....C-3
LUFKIN....G-4
LULING....E-5
MADISONVILLE....F-4
MARATHON....B-5
MARFA....B-5
MARLIN....F-4
MASON....D-4
MATADOR....D-2
MCALLEN....E-7
MCCAMEY....C-4
MEMPHIS....D-2
MENARD....D-4
MERTZON....D-4
MEXIA....F-4
MIAMI....D-1
MIDLAND....C-3
MINEOLA....F-3
MISSION....E-7
MISSOURI CITY....F-5
MONAHANS....B-4
MOUNT PLEASANT....G-3
MULESHOE....C-2
NACOGDOCHES....G-4
NAVASOTA....F-4
NEW BRAUNFELS....E-5
NIXON....E-5
ODESSA....C-4
OLTON....C-2
ORANGE....G-5
PADUCAH....D-2
PALACIOS....F-6
PALESTINE....F-4
PAMPA....C-1
PARIS....F-2
PASADENA....G-5
PEARSALL....E-5
PECOS....B-4
PERRYTON....D-1
PLAINVIEW....C-2

Places Index

PLEASANTON E-5
PORT ARTHUR G-5
PORT ISABEL F-7
PORT LAVACA F-6
PORTLAND F-6
POST C-3
PRESIDIO B-5
RALLS C-2
RANKIN C-4
RAYMONDVILLE E-7
REFUGIO F-6
RICHMOND F-5
RIO GRANDE CITY ...E-7
ROBSTOWN E-6
ROCKDALE F-4
ROCKPORT F-6
ROUND ROCK E-4
RUSK G-4
SAN ANGELO D-4
SANANTONIO E-5
SAN AUGUSTINE G-4
SAN BENITO E-7
SAN MARCOS E-5
SANDERSON C-5
SARITA E-7
SEALY F-5
SEGUIN E-5
SEMINOLE A-4
SEYMOUR D-3
SHERMAN F-2
SIERRA BLANCA A-4
SILSBEE G-4
SINTON E-6
SLATON C-3
SNYDER D-3
SOCORRO A-4
SONORA D-4
STAMFORD D-3
STANTON C-3
STEPHENVILLE E-3
STERLING CITY C-4
STRATFORD A-1
STUDY BUTTE B-5
SULPHUR SPRINGS ...F-3
SWEETWATER D-3
TAYLOR E-4
TEMPLE E-4
TERREL F-3
TEXARKANA G-3
THROCKMORTON E-3
TULIA C-2
TYLER F-3
UVALDE D-5
VAN HORN B-4
VERNON D-3
VICTORIA F-6
WACO E-4
WAXAHACHIE F-3
WHARTON F-5
WHEELER D-1
WICHITA FALLS E-2
WOODVILLE G-4
ZAPATA D-7
ZAVALLA G-4

UTAH
BIGWATER B-7
BLANDING E-6
BLUFF D-6
BOUNTIFUL B-2
CASTLE DALE C-4
COALVILLE C-2
COLTON C-3
COVE FORT B-5
CRESCENT JUNCTION.D-5
DELTA C-3
DUCHESNE D-3
DUTCH JOHN E-2
EMERY C-5
EPHRAIM C-4
EUREKA B-3
FAIRVIEW C-4
FERRON C-5
FILLMORE B-5
FREMONT JUNCTION ..C-5
FRUITLAND D-3
GARDEN CITY C-1
GLENDALE B-6
GREEN RIVER D-4
GUNNISON B-4
HATCH B-6
HEBER CITY C-2
HELPER C-4
HOLDEN B-5
HUNTINGTON C-4
HURRICANE A-7

JUNCTION B-5
KANAB B-7
LAYTON B-2
LOGAN C-2
LYNNDYL B-4
MEXICAN HAT D-7
MOAB E-5
MONTICELLO D-6
MORGAN B-2
MOUNT CARMEL B-7
MYTON D-3
NEPHI B-3
OGDEN B-2
PANGUITCH B-6
PINTURA A-6
PRICE C-4
PROVO C-3
RICHMOND B-1
ROOSEVELT D-3
ROY B-2
SALINA C-5
SALT LAKE CITY C-3
SANDY C-3
SCIPIO B-4
SNOWVILLE B-1
SPANISH FORK B-3
SPRINGVILLE C-3
ST. GEORGE A-7
TREMONTON B-1
VERNAL E-3
WELLINGTON D-4
WENDOVER B-3

VERMONT
ALBURG A-1
BARRE C-3
BENNINGTON A-4
BRANDON A-4
BRATTLEBORO B-7
BURLINGTON A-3
CHARLOTTE A-3
CHESTER B-6
ESSEX JUNCTION A-2
GRAND ISLE A-2
LANCASTER D-2
LUDLOW B-5
MARSHFIELD B-3
MIDDLEBURY A-3
MONTPELIER B-3
NORTH STRATFORD.D-1
NORTON D-1
RUTLAND B-5
SHELBURNE A-3
ST. JOHNSBURY D-2
VERGENNES A-3
WALLINGFORD A-5
WILMINGTON B-7
WOODSTOCK B-5

VIRGINIA
ABINGDON B-4
ACCOMAC G-3
ALEXANDRIA F-1
ALTAVISTA D-3
AMHERST............D-3
ARLINGTON F-1
ASHLAND E-2
BEDFORD D-3
BIG STONE GAP A-3
BLACKSBURG C-3
BLUEFIELD C-3
BOWLING GREEN F-2
BOYCE E-1
BRISTOL B-4
BROOKNEAL E-3
BUENA VISTA D-3
CHARLOTTESVILLE ...E-2
CHATHAM D-4
CHESAPEAKE G-4
CLARKSVILLE E-4
COVINGTON C-3
CREWE E-3
CUCKOO E-2
CULPEPER E-2
CUMBERLAND E-3
DANVILLE D-4
EASTVILLE G-3
EMPORIA F-4
EXMORE G-3
FORK UNION E-3
FRANKLIN F-4
FRANKLIN D-2
FREDERICKSBURG E-2
GATE CITY B-4
HAMPTON G-3
HANOVER F-3

HANSONVILLE........B-3
HARRISONBURG E-2
HILLSVILLE C-4
HOPEWELL F-3
INDEPENDENCE B-4
KIPTOPEKE G-3
LEESBURG...........E-1
LEXINGTON D-3
LOVINGSTON E-3
LYNCHBURG D-3
MARTINSVILLE D-4
MIDDLEBURG E-1
MONTEREY D-2
NEW MARKET E-2
NEWPORT NEWS F-3
NORFOLK G-3
PETERSBURG E-3
PORTSMOUTH F-3
RADFORD C-3
REEDVILLE G-2
RICHMOND F-3
ROANOKE D-3
ROCKY MOUNT D-3
RUSTBURG D-3
SALUDA F-3
SOUTH BOSTON D-4
SOUTH HILL E-4
SPERRYVILLE E-2
STANARDSVILLE E-2
STAUNTON D-2
STUART C-4
SUFFOLK F-4
TAPPAHANNOCK F-2
TAZEWELL B-3
TROUTVILLE D-3
VANSANT B-3
VIRGINIA BEACH G-3
WARM SPRINGS D-2
WARRENTON E-2
WAVERLY F-3
WAYNESBORO E-2
WINCHESTER E-1
WISE B-3
WYLLIESBURG E-4
WYTHEVILLE B-3

WASHINGTON
ABERDEEN A-3
ALMIRA E-2
ANACORTES B-1
AUBURN C-3
BELLEVUE C-2
BELLINGHAM B-1
BLAINE B-1
BREMERTON B-2
BREWSTER E-2
CATHLAMET B-4
CENTRALIA B-3
CHEHALIS B-4
CHELAN E-2
CHEWELAH F-2
CLARKSTON G-4
CLE ELUM D-3
COLFAX G-3
COLVILLE F-1
CONNELL F-3
COUNTRY HOMES G-2
DAVENPORT F-2
DAYTON F-4
EDMONDS B-2
ELLENSBURG D-3
ELMA B-3
ENTIAT D-2
EPHRATA E-3
EVERETT C-2
FEDERAL WAY B-3
FERNDALE B-1
FORKS A-2
FRIDAY HARBOR B-1
GEORGE E-3
GOLD BAR C-2
GOLDENDALE D-4
GRANDVIEW D-4
HOODSPORT B-3
HOQUIAM A-3
KALAMA B-4
KELSO B-4
KENNEWICK E-4
LACEY B-3
LAGRANDE B-3
LEAVENWORTH D-2
LONGVIEW B-4
MARYSVILLE C-2
MESA E-4
MINERAL C-3
MORTON C-4

MOSES LAKE.........E-3
MOUNT VERNON B-1
MUKILTEO C-2
NEAH BAY A-1
NEWPORT G-2
OAK HARBOR B-2
OCEAN PARK A-4
OCEAN SHORES A-3
OKANOGAN E-2
OLYMPIA B-3
OMAK E-1
OPPORTUNITY G-2
OROVILLE E-1
OTHELLO E-3
PACKWOOD C-4
PASCO F-4
POMEROY G-4
PORT ANGELES B-2
PORT HADLOCK B-2
PORT TOWNSEND B-2
PROSSER E-4
PULLMAN G-3
QUINCY E-3
RAYMOND B-3
REDMOND C-2
RENTON C-3
RICHLAND E-4
RIMROCK D-3
RITZVILLE F-3
ROSALIA G-3
SEATTLE B-2
SEQUIM B-2
SHELTON B-3
SKYKOMISH C-2
SNOHOMISH C-2
SOUTH CLE ELUM....D-3
SPANAWAY C-3
SPOKANE F-2
SPRAGUE F-3
SUMNER C-3
SUNNYSIDE E-4
SYDNEY B-1
TACOMA B-3
TAHOLAH A-3
TOLEDO B-4
TOPPENISH D-4
TUMWATER B-3
VANCOUVER B-5
WALLA WALLA F-4
WAPATO D-4
WENATCHEE D-3
WHITE SALMON C-5
WILBUR F-2
YAKIMA D-4

WEST VIRGINIA
ANSTED C-5
BRIDGEPORT D-3
BUCKHANNON C-3
CAMERON C-2
CHARLESTON B-4
CLARKSBURG C-3
DELBARTON A-5
ELKINS D-3
FAIRMONT C-3
FRANKLIN D-4
GILBERT B-5
GRAFTON D-3
HARMAN D-3
HARPERS FERRY F-3
HARTS A-5
HILLSBORO D-4
HUNTINGTON A-4
HUTTONSVILLE C-4
KERMIT A-5
KEYSER E-3
LEON B-4
LEWISBURG C-5
MARTINSBURG F-3
MOOREFIELD E-3
MORGANTOWN D-2
MOUNDSVILLE C-2
MOUNT NEBO C-5
NEW MARTINSVILLE.C-2
OAK HILL B-5
PARKERSBURG B-3
PHILIPPI D-3
POINT PLEASANT A-4
PRINCETON B-5
RAINELLE C-5

RAVENSWOOD B-3
ROMNEY E-3
SOPHIA B-5
SPENCER B-3
UNION C-5
WELCH B-6
WHEELING C-2

WISCONSIN
ANTIGO C-3
APPLETON D-4
ASHLAND B-1
BARABOO C-5
BEAVER DAM C-5
BELOIT C-6
BLACK RIVER FALLS B-4
BRUCE B-3
BRULE B-1
CAMERON B-3
CASPER E-3
CHILTON D-4
CHIPPEWA FALLS B-3
CLINTONVILLE D-3
COLOMA C-4
COLUMBUS C-5
CRANDON C-3
CRIVITZ D-3
DENMARK D-4
DICKEYVILLE B-6
DODGEVILLE B-5
EAGLE RIVER C-2
EAU CLAIRE B-3
ELKHORN D-5
ELLSWORTH A-3
FOND DU LAC C-5
FORT ATKINSON D-5
FRIENDSHIP C-4
GALESVILLE B-4
GRAFTON D-5
GREEN BAY D-4
HAYWARD B-2
KENOSHA D-6
LA CROSSE B-4
LADYSMITH B-3
LAND O' LAKES C-2
LAONA C-3
MADISON C-5
MANITOWOC D-4
MARINETTE D-3
MARION C-4
MARSHFIELD B-3
MAUSTON B-4
MEDFORD B-3
MELLEN B-2
MENASHA D-4
MERRILL C-3
MILWAUKEE D-5
MONROE C-5
NEILLSVILLE B-4
NEW LONDON C-4
OCONTO D-3
OSHKOSH D-4
PEMBINE D-2
PITTSVILLE B-4
PLATTEVILLE B-5
PLOVER C-4
PORT WASHINGTON ..D-5
PORTAGE C-5
PRAIRIE DU CHIEN ..B-5
PRENTICE C-3
RACINE D-5
READSTOWN B-5
RICE LAKE B-3
RICHLAND CENTER ..B-5
SAUK CITY C-5
SCHOFIELD C-3
SHAWANO D-3
SHEBOYGAN D-4
SPARTA B-4
SPOONER A-2
STEVENS POINT C-4
SUPERIOR A-1
TURTLE LAKE A-3
UNITY C-3
VIROQUA B-5
WAUKESHA D-5
WAUPACA C-4
WAUPUN C-4
WAUSAU C-3
WAUSAUKEE D-3
WEST BEND D-5
WINCHESTER C-2
WISCONSIN DELLS ...C-4

WITTENBERG C-3

WYOMING
AFTON A-3
ALCOVA E-3
ALPINE A-3
ARLINGTON E-4
BAGGS D-5
BANNER D-1
BONDURANT B-3
BORDER A-4
BOSLER F-4
BUFFALO D-1
BURRIS C-2
CASPER E-3
CHEYENNE F-5
CHUGWATER F-4
CODY C-1
COKEVILLE A-4
CRESTON JUNCTION D-4
CROWHEART B-2
DANIEL B-3
DEAVER C-1
DOUGLAS F-3
DUBOIS B-2
EDEN C-4
ELK MOUNTAIN E-4
EMBLEM C-1
EVANSTON A-5
FARSON B-4
FORT WASHAKIE B-3
FOUR CORNERS F-2
FREEDOM A-3
GILLETTE E-1
GLENDO F-3
GREEN RIVER B-4
GREYBULL D-1
GROVER A-3
HANNA E-4
JACKSON B-2
JAY EM G-3
KAYCEE E-2
KEMMERER B-4
KIRBY D-2
LAMONT D-4
LANDER C-3
LARAMIE F-4
LITTLE AMERICA B-4
LOVELL C-1
LUSK F-3
LYMAN B-5
MAMMOTH A-1
MANDERSON D-1
MERIDEN F-4
MONETA D-3
MOORCROFT F-1
MORAN B-2
MUDDY GAP D-3
NATRONA E-3
NEWCASTLE F-2
OPAL B-4
ORIN F-3
PINE BLUFFS G-5
PINEDALE B-3
POINT OF ROCKS C-4
RANCHESTER D-1
RAWLINS D-4
REDBIRD F-2
RIVERTON C-3
RIVERVIEW F-2
ROCK RIVER E-4
ROCK SPRINGS C-4
SAGE A-4
SHERIDAN D-1
SHOSHONI D-2
SLATER F-4
SUNDANCE F-1
SWEETWATER
  STATION D-3
TEN SLEEP D-2
THAYNE A-3
THERMOPOLIS D-2
TORRINGTON F-4
TOWER JUNCTION B-1
UPTON F-2
VAN TASSELL G-3
WALCOTT D-4
WALTMAN D-3
WHEATLAND F-4
WINCHESTER C-2
WORLAND D-2

CANADA
ALMA E-4
ARCTIC BAY D-1
ARVIAT D-2

BAKER LAKE D-2
BATHURST INLET C-1
BRANDON C-4
CALGARY B-3
CAMBRIDGE BAY C-1
CAMPBELL RIVER A-3
CAPE DORSET E-2
CAPE DYER E-1
CARMACKS A-1
CHANNEL-PORT-
  AUXBASQUES......G-4
CHARLOTTETOWN F-4
CHESTERFIELD
  INLET ....-2
CHIBOUGAMAU E-3
CHISASIBI E-3
CHURCHILL D-3
CLYDE RIVER E-1
COPPERMINE C-1
CORAL HARBOUR....D-2
CORNER BROOK F-3
DAWSON A-1
DAWSON CREEK A-3
DEASE LAKE A-2
EDMONTON B-3
FARO B-1
FLIN FLON C-3
FORT FRANKLIN B-1
FORT GOOD HOPE ...B-1
FORT MCMURRAY B-3
FORT MCPHERSON ...B-1
FORT SEVERN D-3
FORT SIMPSON B-2
FORT SMITH C-2
FREDERICTON F-4
GASPE E-4
GRAND FALLS G-3
GRANDE PRAIRIE B-3
HALIFAX G-4
HAPPY VALLEY -
  GOOSE BAY E-3
HAY RIVER B-2
HOLMAN C-1
HOPEDALE F-3
IGLOOLIK D-1
INUKJUAK E-3
INUVIK A-1
IQALUIT E-2
IVUJIVIK E-2
KAMLOOPS A-3
KAPUSKASING E-4
KENORA D-4
KITIMAT A-2
KUUJJUAQ F-3
LA RONGE C-3
LABRADOR CITY E-3
LAKE HARBOUR E-2
LETHBRIDGE B-4
LONDON E-5
MARYSTOWN G-4
MEANDER RIVER B-2
MONCTON F-4
MONTRÉAL E-4
MOOSONEE D-4
NAIN F-2
NORTH BAY E-4
OTTAWA E-4
PANGNIRTUNG E-1
PEACE RIVER B-3
PELLY BAY D-1
PICKLE LAKE D-3
PORT BUNWELL F-2
PORT HARDY A-3
PORT INLET D-3
PRINCE ALBERT C-3
PRINCE GEORGE A-3
PRINCE RUPERT A-2
QUAQTAQ E-2
QUÉBEC E-4
QUEEN CHARLOTTE. A-2
RED DEER B-3
RED LAKE D-3
REGINA C-4
REPULSE BAY D-2
RESOLUTION
  ISLAND F-2
RIVIÈRE-DU-LOUP ...F-4
ROUYN-NORANDA E-4
SAINT JOHN F-4
SASKATOON C-4
SAULT STE. MARIE ..F-4
SHERBROOKE F-4
SPENCE BAY D-1
ST. ANTHONY F-3
ST. JOHN'S G-3
SWIFT CURRENT B-4

SYDNEY G-4
TESLIN A-2
THE PAS C-3
THOMPSON C-3
THUNDER BAY D-4
TIMMINS D-4
TORONTO E-5
TRAIL B-3
TROIS-RIVIERES E-4
TRURO F-4
TUNGSTEN B-1
TWIN FALLS F-3
URANIUM CITY B-2
VANCOUVER A-3
VICTORIA A-3
WATSON LAKE A-2
WAWA D-4
WHITEHORSE A-1
WILLIAMS LAKE A-3
WINDSOR E-5
WINNIPEG C-4
YARMOUTH F-4
YELLOWKNIFE C-2
YORK FACTORY D-3

MEXICO
ACAPONETA C-3
ACAPULCO D-5
AGUACALIENTES C-3
ALVARADO F-4
CAMPECHE G-3
CANCUN G-3
CARAPAN D-4
CHETUMAL G-4
CHIHUAHUA C-2
CIUDAD CAMARGO...C-2
CIUDAD
  CONSTITUCÍON A-3
CIUDAD MADERO E-3
CIUDAD MANTE E-3
CIUDAD OBREGON...B-2
CIUDAD VICTORIA ...D-4
COLIMA D-4
CUERNAVACA D-4
CULICÁN C-2
DURANGO C-3
ENSENADA A-1
ESCÁRCEGA G-4
FELIPE CARRILLO
  PUERTO G-4
FRESNILLO C-3
GUADALAJARA D-4
GUAYMAS B-2
HERMOSILO B-2
JIMÉNEZ C-1
JUÁREZ C-1
JUCHITAN F-5
LAPAZ B-3
LEON D-4
LOS MOCHIS C-2
MANZANILLO C-4
MATAMOROS E-2
MAZATLÁN C-3
MÉRIDA F-3
MEXICALI A-1
MEXICO CITY D-4
MONTERREY D-2
MORELIA D-4
NAVOJOA B-2
NOGALES B-1
NUEVO LAREDO D-2
OAXACA E-5
PACHUCA E-4
PETO G-3
PLAYA AZUL D-4
PUEBLA E-4
SAN CRISTÓBAL
  DE LAS CASAS F-5
SAN LOUIS POTOSÍ..D-4
SANTA ROSALÍA A-2
SATILLO E-3
TAMPICO E-3
TAPACHULA F-5
TEHUACÁN E-4
TEHUANTEPEC E-5
TEPIC C-3
TIJUANA A-1
TORREON C-2
TUXPAN E-4
TUXTEPEC E-4
TUXTLA GUTIERREZ .F-5
VALLADOLID F-3
VERACRUZ E-4
VILLAHERMOSA F-5
ZACATECAS C-3

Answer Page

Page 3

S E L M A
O
N
T
G
O
M
E
R   T U S C A L O O S A   D O T H A N
P H E N I X C I T Y

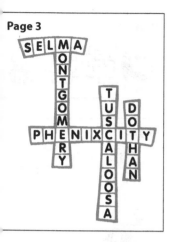

Page 4

Page 6
Hot Springs

Page 8
1. Wyoming
2. Nebraska
3. Kansas
4. New Mexico
5. Arizona
6. Utah
7. Oklahoma

Page 10
14

Page 11

Page 12

PEACH

Page 13
Volcano
Suntan Lotion
Sea Turtle
Whale
Fish
Sunglasses
Sea Shell
Palm Tree
Beach Ball
Starfish
Flower
Sparky

Page 14

Page 15
Champaign	D-4
Chicago	D-1
Decatur	C-4
Paris	D-4
Rock Falls	C-2
Springfield	B-4
Waterloo	B-6

Page 17

Page 18
Wyatt Earp

Page 19
Daniel Boone

Page 20

Page 21

Page 22

Page 24
THE GREAT LAKES

M I C H I G A N   O N T A R I O
H U R O N   S U P E R I O R   E R I E

Page 25
St. Cloud
Red Wing
Jackson
Cook
Duluth

Page 26

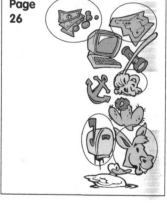

Page 27
1. East
2. 40
3. Star
4. Illinois

Page 28
Cowboy

Page 29

Answer Page

Page 30

Austin	C-3
Carson City	A-4
Eureka	C-3
Jackpot	D-1
Reno	A-3
Sparks	A-3
Topaz Lake	A-4

Page 34

C AMDEN
ATLANTICCITY
CHESTER
TRENTON
OCEANCITY
NEWBRUNSWICK

Page 35

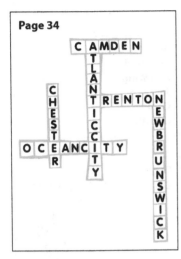

Page 37
Kitty Hawk

Page 39
Fall Football

Page 40
Pickup Truck
Oil Well
Bird
Pitchfork
Bale Of Hay
Indian Headdress
Rooster
Pig

Page 41

Page 42
Punxsutawney Phil

Page 44

Page 45
Mount Rushmore

Page 46
Drums

Page 47

Page 48

Page 50
1. Roanoke
2. North Carolina
3. True
4. 33
5. West Virginia
6. Atlantic

Page 51
1. Yakima
2. Seattle
3. Spokane
4. Everett
5. Olympia
6. Tacoma

Page 52

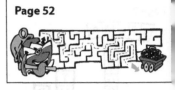

Page 53

Page 54
1. Cheyenne
2. Rawlins
3. Jackson
4. Laramie
5. Sundance

Page 55